New Magic

ILLUSTRATED BY
William M. Hutchinson

New Magic

By ESMA RIDEOUT BOOTH

Friendship Press   NEW YORK

Library of Congress Catalog Card Number: 59-6598

Contents

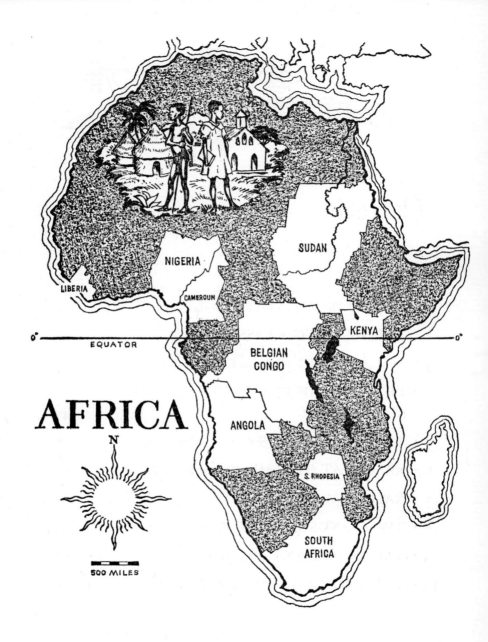

LIBERIA

NIGERIA

CAMEROUN

SUDAN

KENYA

0°   EQUATOR   0°

BELGIAN
CONGO

AFRICA

N

ANGOLA

S. RHODESIA

SOUTH
AFRICA

500 MILES

Africa

The stories in this book are about boys and girls who live in the part of Africa that lies south of the Sahara Desert.

In this part of Africa live more than 200 million people. Over the long centuries, the people have been divided from one another by rivers and lakes, forests and deserts. So they have come to live in tribes that speak different languages and follow different customs.

Africa south of the Sahara is divided into many countries. Some are republics, like Liberia, Sudan, and newly free Ghana. Most of the countries, however, are related to one or another of the European nations. In all these countries, the people feel an urge to become more and more self-governing.

Africa is changing very quickly. The people of Africa are learning to speak common languages. They are learning new ways of earning a livelihood, new ways of keeping healthy, new ways of working together. They are learning to read, and one of the books they like to read is the Bible. As they learn, they are dropping the old ways of fear that bound them for so long—fear of bad magic, fear of evil spirits, fear of the witch doctor. The African people have found a new kind of magic, a good magic. It is the magic of learning.

SUDAN

Adyeng lives in the Sudan near a river that flows into the Nile. He goes to a mission school.

The Sudan is one of the countries of Africa that has become independent. In the northern part, near Egypt, there are many people who are Muslim in religion. In the southern part, near the Congo, there are not so many Muslims. In this part live people of many tribes, speaking different languages.

Adyeng and his family belong to one of these tribes. They live in a small river village. If Adyeng did not go to school, he would probably take care of the cows at home, since cattle are important in his tribe.

In his country the roads are poor, and in the rainy season some are impassable. So the people do most of their traveling in dugout canoes on the rivers, as Adyeng and his friends did.

1 Adyeng's Vacation

Adyeng stood beside the canoe at the river's edge. Four boys were already standing in it, and three more were putting in their bundles. Their school in the Sudan had closed for vacation that very day. They were ready to start on a two day trip back to their villages. For a few weeks no more schoolwork, no more responsibilities! Adyeng rejoiced.

"Adyeng, will you take this package of books and give them to Teacher Obwony in your village?"

Adyeng looked at the well wrapped package the young missionary teacher was holding out to him. Surely the missionary must know that a dugout canoe with eight boys in it was no place for a package of precious books!

"You know what these books will mean to your village, Adyeng?" said the missionary.

"Yes," said Adyeng slowly, and he reached for the books. He did not wish to be responsible for them, but he said, "I'll do my best to deliver them safely."

"I'll understand if they get wet," said the missionary. "Accidents have happened to me, you know, even in the motor launch."

He smiled at Adyeng, and Adyeng had to smile back as he remembered the motor launch accident, when the box of school supplies had got wet. Everyone had hurried to open the box and spread the supplies in the sun to dry.

"Thank you," said the missionary. "I hope you will find your village different now that Obwony lives there."

Adyeng stepped into the canoe and sat down. One of the older boys was the leader, and he had selected four boys to paddle first.

"Go well!" called the missionary from the river's edge.

"Stay well!" shouted all the boys, as they pushed out into the water.

Adyeng held the package of books and thought about the missionary's words. Would his village truly be different now that a Christian teacher lived there all the time? When he had been home during the last vacation, it had been difficult to stand up for the new ways he had learned. Back at school once again, he had felt a little ashamed that he had not been braver.

One of the boys lifted his paddle quickly, and some water splashed onto the books. Adyeng looked at them in alarm.

"Put this around them," said his friend Yor, passing Adyeng his blue shirt.

"The wrapping on the outside is the strong paper that

keeps the water out," said Adyeng, "but it is good to protect the books as much as we can."

Adyeng put Yor's shirt around the package and took off his own and added it. It was warm on the river, and clothes were a bother. In his home village he would wear little. He would have a vacation from clothes as well as school.

Riding in the canoe was pleasant, and Adyeng watched the green shore slip by. Once he saw a small antelope standing near a clump of bushes for a moment before it disappeared. He watched the pelicans fishing in shallow water with their long flat beaks.

At the bend in the river Adyeng became one of the paddlers and Yor held the books. When the sun stood overhead and it was very hot, they paddled close to the shore and rested a little while in the shade of the trees.

"Look out!" shouted Adyeng suddenly. He gave a great push with his paddle just as a crocodile slipped from the high grass into the water in front of them. The canoe swayed as the boys lifted their paddles to scare the animal. With a slither and a splash, the crocodile slid away, and the excitement died down. Adyeng looked anxiously at the books.

"No damage done," said Yor cheerfully. "Nothing wet but our shirts."

Two other shirts were donated to protect the books as the paddlers pushed out into the deep water again.

The afternoon passed quickly. Sometimes the boys sang, and sometimes talked of school and of the vacation ahead.

The sun was halfway down the sky when the paddlers
arrived at the village where two of the boys lived. Here they
planned to spend the night. As they came close to shore, they
saw some village men fishing from canoes. How good that big
fish would taste later, thought Adyeng, as he watched a man
spear a Nile perch.

The boys pulled the canoe well up the bank into the tall
grass. Adyeng picked up the package of books and unwrapped
the shirts of the village boys. The package was still wrapped in
his shirt and Yor's.

"Let's have a swim!" cried one of the boys. He was in the
water almost as soon as he said it. The others splashed in after

him. There was a safe place to swim, for the village folk had
made a bamboo enclosure as a protection from the crocodiles.

Adyeng hesitated a moment. Several bundles were lying
where the boys had dropped them, but he felt that the shore
was not dry enough for books. He pushed through the bushes
and placed his package under a big palm tree close to the path.

When he plunged in, the water felt good on his hot shoulders and arms. He dived and swam and shouted with the rest.
Then he helped pull the fishing boats up on shore and
admired the catch of the fishermen.

The sun was almost down when the boys left the water.
Adyeng ran for his package. He stopped, puzzled. There was

the big palm tree near the path. But where were the books? He looked anxiously around. There were no books!

"What's the matter?" asked Yor, coming up beside him.

Adyeng swallowed hard. Oh, why had he let the important package out of his sight!

"The books are gone," he said in a shaking voice. "I put them right there."

"You must have put them under another tree," said Yor matter-of-factly.

But although both boys looked all around, they could not find the books. The other boys and a few of the village men came to see what was wrong.

"Someone going along the path has picked them up," said one man.

"What would anyone want with books?" asked another. "No one around here can read."

"They would not know the package had books in it," said Yor. "Perhaps they were after the two shirts."

The man grunted. "You will never see your shirts again, or the books either," he said. "Let's go on into the village. I am hungry, and you boys must be starved."

Adyeng tried not to think about how hungry he was.

"I am going to follow the path and try to catch whoever took the books," he said.

"It will soon be dark," objected one man. "It wouldn't be safe."

"You won't find the books," began another. But one of the

village boys who had come from school with Adyeng interrupted.

"There's the little village over the hill," he said. "You know the man Deng? I bet he or his sons took the package. He has taken things before."

A murmur of agreement went around the group.

"Lead me there," said Adyeng.

"I'd be afraid for just us two to go," answered the boy.

He looked as though he wished he hadn't spoken, but when one of the young men of the village said, "Come along," he followed. Yor did not say anything but walked behind Adyeng on the narrow path.

As the four hurried forward, the young man told about a lion that had been killed not far away the day before.

"I'm glad he is dead," said Yor jokingly, but Adyeng knew that, like himself, Yor was trying hard to be brave. Where one lion had been, there might well be another. Perhaps the young man wanted them to know how brave he was to come with them, thought Adyeng. He felt grateful but did wish for less talk about lions.

Soon the lights of a fire shone out ahead of them in the gathering darkness.

"That is Deng's house," said the young man in a low voice. He stopped, and the boy stopped, too.

"Aren't you coming with us?" asked Yor.

"Deng has powerful medicine," said the young man uneasily. "He can make a person fall dead just by saying words."

Adyeng looked at the boy from school, who must know better than to believe that. But the boy turned away, saying, "I'll wait for you here."

Adyeng couldn't really blame him. He tried to think of the reassuring words about God's care that he had learned in the Bible classes at school. But somehow here on the path the stories of witchcraft that he had heard all his life seemed to crowd those words out of his mind. He shut his lips tight. He felt hot all over, and suddenly he was cold and shivering. But he walked steadily on. Yor was close behind him. He was the kind of friend to have!

Around the fire sat an old man and his three sons. They were looking at something, and as the boys watched, the old man threw down a large piece of paper.

"They have the books, all right," whispered Yor.

Adyeng reached for his friend's hand. For a moment he felt so afraid that he was not sure whether or not he was glad to have found the books. Then he stepped quickly up to the fire. Yor was close beside him.

"Good evening," he said politely.

No answer came from the men, who did not even look at them. The old man was holding a New Testament.

"Will you please give us our books?" said Adyeng and was surprised that his voice did not tremble.

He had a great desire to turn and run, but instead he said, "That book you hold is a book full of wisdom and power." It would not be right to use the Bible to frighten the men, but those words were certainly true, thought Adyeng. "It tells us many things about God," he went on.

"Keep our shirts, but give back the books to us who can read them," said Yor.

One of the young men spoke in a low voice to his father, and the old man reluctantly gave up the New Testament. Then the son picked up three smaller books that Adyeng knew were first readers and put them and the New Testament on the ground a little way from the fire.

Adyeng stepped forward and took the books and backed away. "Thank you," he said.

Again there was no answer. The four men began to discuss loudly what they should do with the shirts.

Adyeng and Yor hurried back to the two who were waiting anxiously. Their friends were surprised to see the books.

"The old man may cause you harm yet," the young man said fearfully. "He can use his evil power even though you are miles away."

Adyeng did not believe that the old man could harm him by witchcraft, but he was glad enough to hurry away with the others.

It was dark when they reached the village. Adyeng kept the books beside him while he ate the good fish and mush that were waiting. When he lay down to sleep, he put the books between him and Yor.

The next day, the village boys gave Adyeng some cloth to protect the books, which now had no waterproof paper around them. With only six boys continuing the trip, there was more paddling for each one, but always someone held the books. At noontime, two more boys left, and by the middle of the afternoon, Adyeng knew that they were close to his own village. It was good that Yor's home was only a short distance beyond.

As soon as the canoe touched the shore, Adyeng got out, and his family and friends crowded around him. He held the books carefully as he answered their excited greetings.

"Where is Teacher Obwony?" he asked, anxious to give over the big responsibility of taking care of the books.

"He goes once a week to preach in the village beyond the hill," said his father. "He will be back tonight."

"Come! Food is waiting for you," said his mother.

Adyeng's younger sister, Aba, with baby brother on her back, knelt as she handed him food, as she always did to their father. It did make Adyeng feel important, but a little uncomfortable, too. He smiled at her and she smiled back.

Then she looked at the books and said, "I'm glad you brought the books. Will you teach me to read?"

"Don't you go to Teacher Obwony's school?" he asked.

"No. I have to take care of the baby while Mother works in the garden. The boys all go to school, but only two girls do."

"I'll help you all I can," promised Adyeng. "I'll ask Teacher Obwony to show me how to teach you to read this vacation."

"I'm glad you have come home," Aba said happily.

Adyeng finished eating and opened one of the readers. He showed Aba the pictures and taught her some words.

Early the next morning, Adyeng walked through the village. He passed by the cow barn. He thought of the fun he would have going with the other boys to care for the cows in the long free days of vacation. Or would the days be all free after all, he wondered, thinking of his sister.

He found Obwony sitting near his house. He handed over the precious books with a happy feeling. Obwony looked just as happy to receive them.

"I almost lost the books," said Adyeng. He told the teacher how Deng had taken them.

"I'm glad you were brave and got them back," said Obwony. "Here in the village I have been trying to make the people understand that they do not need to be afraid of witchcraft."

"I wasn't brave. I was afraid," confessed Adyeng.

Suddenly he laughed. It was true that he had been afraid, but he had done what he knew to be right just the same. Perhaps that was being brave after all.

NAMES IN THE STORY

Aba	A-ba
Adyeng	A-dyeng
Deng	deng
Obwony	oh-BWOH-nee
Sudan	SOO-DAN
Yor	yor

KENYA

All over Africa, people are learning to read.
The children go to school, but there are not
enough schools for all who want to go.

The older people cannot go to school like the children, but many
manage to learn to read.

A few years ago there was great trouble in Kenya. Many people
were not satisfied with the laws of the country. The troubles have
quieted down, but some men, like Neno's father, are still not
satisfied.

There are people of different kinds living in Kenya—some from
Europe, some from India, and some whose ancestors have been in
Africa for centuries. Of course there are more of these Africans
than anyone else. Many of them have to live on tracts of land,
called reserves, that are set apart for their use.

2 The Reading Class

Neno stopped grinding the kernels of grain between the stones. The drum was calling. She lifted her head to listen.

"Come! Come to church! The missionaries are here today. Come with haste!" The drum rang out its message in the little village in Kenya where Neno lived.

Neno glanced quickly at her mother, who had just returned from the garden. Mother had put baby brother on a mat and was spreading corn out to dry.

"Mother will go to church today," thought Neno. She knew that though Mother had never said that she wanted to be a Christian, she always went to the meetings unless Father was angry and said that she could not.

Neno sighed. It seemed to her that her father was angry all the time lately. Since he had come back from his stay in the city, no one could please him. And last night he had said that she had gone to school long enough. It was true that she had finished the four years, which were all the village school provided, and that was more than most girls had. But she had been hoping that she could go on to boarding school at the mission station.

This morning her father was away, so there was no reason why she and her mother could not go to church. If he came home and there was no food ready for him, he might be very angry indeed, but there would be time enough to worry about that later.

Her mother was listening to the drum sending out its message. "Come! Come to church!"

The drummer in the village on the other side had heard it and was beating out the message to the people farther away. Drummers in the next village and the next would send it along until all the people near enough to come to church would hear it.

Neno's little brother and sister came running. Mother picked up the baby and started toward the path.

Neno gave her sister's arm a jerk. "Hurry up," she said. "Do you want us to be late?" Her sister began to cry in a loud voice. "Oh, stop it. I didn't hurt you," said Neno impatiently.

Neno's mother looked at her but did not say anything. She understood about Neno's longing for school and knew why she was feeling so cross. Suddenly Neno was ashamed. After all, her mother had never had any chance at all to go to school, and she wanted to learn, too. She was always asking Neno to repeat the Bible stories she learned at school.

Out on the path others were walking toward the church—

men and women and children. Neno began to feel better and joined in when someone started a song.

They came to the church, and Neno was glad to see the pastor from the mission station. He was a man of their tribe and he always told good stories. Then she noticed three missionaries, a man and two women, standing by the church door. One was Miss Ford, who was in charge of the boarding school. Usually she was the one Neno wanted to see most. Now she thought of her father's words and did not feel like talking with her.

But Miss Ford caught sight of her and called, "Neno! Neno!"

Neno walked slowly toward her.

"Neno, I have good news for you. You passed the examinations for entering the boarding school with high marks."

Neno swallowed hard but did not look up.

"Aren't you happy?" asked Miss Ford in surprise. "There isn't room for all the girls who want to come, but there is a place for you."

Neno tried to answer, but there was a big lump in her throat.

"Yes, I'm glad," she began.

People were crowding into the church, and someone pushed between Neno and the teacher. Neno was relieved that she did not have to say anything more just then.

She looked for her brother and sister, but they were playing happily under a tree with other children, and she left them alone. She slipped into the church and took a seat a little behind her mother and the baby. The pastor talked about what it meant to be a Christian. After some singing, the missionary told about the new classes that were being started for the grownups who wanted to learn to read.

The baby began to fuss, and Neno glanced toward him. Her mother was leaning forward, her eyes intent on the missionary. Was Mother interested in learning to read, Neno wondered. She listened and heard that the classes would be held here in the schoolhouse beside the church. The baby started to cry. Mother turned to see where Neno was.

Neno looked the other way. There would be more singing, and perhaps the pastor would tell another story. She didn't want to go out with the baby. But from the corner of her eye she saw that her mother was trying hard to pay attention in spite of the crying baby. Reluctantly Neno moved forward and took the baby. Her mother smiled at her and quickly looked again at the missionary.

Neno walked away from the church so that the crying baby would not disturb anyone. She saw four men standing near a tree on the other side of the schoolhouse, and the one with his back toward her looked like her father. Neno shifted the baby and looked again but saw only three men. Well, even if the other one had been her father, he probably would not leave before she and her mother. He liked to talk too well, telling what he thought the leaders of the country were doing wrong and what they ought to do.

The baby, pleased at being carried around, stopped crying, and Neno went back toward the church. When the singing began again, Mother came out and took the baby.

"Go and sing," she said. "It is your turn."

Neno went inside and began to sing with the others. The missionary finished with a story about Jesus teaching by the seaside. Neno told it to her mother as they walked home.

Father was there before them, but he was talking with the other men of the village and paid no attention to his family. Neno hurried to help her mother cook food, working as carefully as she could. Her mother was a good cook, and Father was accustomed to eating well, either alone or as he sat with the other men.

Soon Mother carried his food to him, and Neno began to serve the children. Mother was looking worried when she returned.

"Was Father cross because we went to church and his food was late?" asked Neno.

"No," replied Mother. She hesitated and went on. "He is sitting with the witch doctor, and they are talking about making some strong medicine."

Neno spoke quickly, "I hope it is not to harm the pastor or his work."

There was no answer. Neno knew that her mother was divided between her old fears of evil spirits and her interest in all that she was learning of Christian ways. In her house, there were still charms to protect those she loved. She did not quite dare to give them up. But charms to harm people were another matter. Neno was sure that her mother would hate to have her father ask the witch doctor for that kind.

When Father came into the yard, he seemed to be thinking of things other than his family and said nothing. Neno finished her work and went to bed. She tried to remember all that the pastor had talked about and said the words of her favorite hymn over and over until she went to sleep.

During the next few days, Father was not home much and talked little when there. Mother was anxious when she knew he was with the witch doctor and even more so when he brought home a tiny horn of medicine and added it to the collection of charms in the corner of the house. Neno was anxious, too, wondering what the new charm was for.

One night the teacher of the village school stopped to talk with Neno and her mother. He was sad when Neno told him that her father said she could not go to the boarding school.

"Let us wait a few days before we send word about it to the missionary," he said.

Mother spoke slowly, "I want to go to the class to learn to read."

Neno stared at her. How could her mother go? Who would cook for her father? Who would do all the work at home?

The teacher was pleased. "Everyone should learn to read," he said. "Your husband was asking about the classes, too."

"I'm afraid it was not for a good reason," said Mother.

All the next day Neno kept thinking of her mother's words.

"I could take care of the children," she said to herself, "but I couldn't cook food as Mother does. Father wouldn't like it at all."

She pushed the thoughts away, but they came back again. She remembered all the times that her mother had let her go to school when most mothers would have kept her home to take care of the small children.

The next morning Neno said to her mother, "It is tomorrow that the classes start. I can manage the work, if you want to go."

She was half hoping that Mother would say that she was too young to take charge of everything. But Mother looked very pleased and began to make plans.

"I will get up early and do all the work I can before I leave. You must watch the children and make everything ready for the evening meal. I will come home quickly after class to prepare the food for your father."

"She must want to learn to read very much," thought Neno as she watched her mother hurry away the next morning.

The children did not give her much time to worry about how angry her father would be if he should come home first and find her mother away. The baby fussed, and the children got into all kinds of mischief. Her little brother burned his hand as he pulled a roasted sweet potato out of the fire, and he cried a long time. Neno was relieved when, in the middle of the afternoon, she saw her mother coming.

Mother laughed and talked while she prepared the food. It was easy enough when there was one to work and one to watch the children, thought Neno. She remembered all the times her mother had worked alone. "But she is older and knows exactly how to do everything," she said to herself.

"I'm glad Father didn't come home first," she said out loud.

Mother stopped laughing. "He will be here before long," she said. "He was in the class at the school."

"He was!" exclaimed Neno. "What was he doing there? Oh, Mother, did he make any trouble?"

"No, he listened well and seemed interested," said her mother, looking as if she were trying to figure it out.

Neno picked up the baby. If her father was trying to use the power of the witch doctor to defeat the reading class, why did he go to it and listen?

A few minutes later, she watched her father coming into the yard. He did not look like a person who was making charms to harm anyone. He spoke pleasantly to the family.

The next days were busy and difficult ones, although each day Neno learned how to manage the work better and how to keep the children out of mischief. Each afternoon, Mother had interesting stories to tell of what had happened at the school. She reported that Father was always in the class. But she always left quickly so that she could be home first.

Once she said—and her voice was proud—"Your father is learning to read better than anyone."

"That is good!" said Neno. "Of course," she thought, "if Father truly wants to learn to read, he will do it faster than anyone else because he is very clever."

The next night Father brought home a little book and sat reading until the food was ready. When he went to talk with the other men, he left the book on the log where he had been sitting.

Mother picked it up. "It is the *Stories of Jesus*," she said. "I have been wanting to have one."

"I think Father left it there so that you could use it, too," said Neno. "Read while there is still a little light. I will finish the work."

"You are a good daughter," said her mother.

Every night after that Father read, and when he went away he left the book. He brought home a book about how to keep well. Neno picked it up and read it very quickly, for it was small with only a few difficult words.

One night Father brought home a bigger book.

"Soon I will be able to read anything," he said. "I do not need my charm any more."

"Your charm? Which one?" asked Neno. Mother looked alarmed.

"The charm I got to give me wisdom so that I could learn well. I do not want to listen forever to people who say one thing today and another tomorrow. I want to read books and papers so that I can find out for myself and tell others what to do."

Neno could not help laughing with relief.

For a few minutes Mother did not say anything, then she spoke softly, "I do not think you ever needed the charm to make you wise. The teacher says that you are the best reader of all, and you have learned faster than anyone he has ever taught. I think you will be a good leader."

Father looked pleased, but he frowned a little at her next words.

"The missionary teacher also said that your daughter is clever and that her examination papers were among the very best."

Neno waited anxiously. Father did not answer at once. Then he looked at her. "You are a good daughter," he said.

"You have cared for the children and worked hard at home. Some day you will be as fine a cook as your mother."

He sat in thought for a few minutes. Then he said, "Our whole family is learning. Yes, Neno, you must go on to school. Learning is good, and I want you to have it."

NAMES IN THE STORY

Kenya	KEE-nyah
Neno	NAY-noh

BELGIAN CONGO

In the Belgian Congo, the people are of many tribes and speak many languages. When the children stay in their own part of the country, they do not think about other languages, since they hear only their own.

But many men, like Mala's father, go to work in the cities and take their families with them. Most of the families continue to speak their own languages at home. But in the mines and smelting plants and shops and banks and all the other places of work, as well as in the schools and churches, a single language is used. A common language is necessary, if the people are to understand each other.

Swahili, a native language, is widely used in parts of the Congo and also in East Africa. The French language, spoken by the Belgian people, is coming to be used more and more in the schools.

The Belgian government has some schools in the cities, but not enough, so it gives help to the mission schools, both Roman Catholic and Protestant. Mala goes to a Protestant mission school, where most of the teachers are African.

3 Mala's Song

Mala closed her arithmetic book and looked happily at the teacher. He had just said that it was the hour for singing. To her that was the best time of the day in her mission school in a city of the Belgian Congo.

"Christmas will soon be here," the teacher was saying. "Our fifth grade has been asked to learn 'Joy to the World.' Then we are to choose our best singers to be in a choir to sing it in the Christmas pageant."

Mala listened as the teacher sang the first stanza. Good! The song was one that her older brother Limo often sang, and she began to hum it. The teacher smiled at her.

"All who know the words of the first stanza, try it with me," he said. Several children began to sing, but only Mala knew all the words to the end.

"I know it in my own language," said one of the girls.

"So do I." The voices were scattered over the room.

"In mine it goes like this."

The teacher clapped his hands for order. "We are singing it in Swahili," he said severely, when there was quiet enough to be heard. Then he smiled. "I am glad so many know it in their own languages, but we can't sing the song in several different languages at once. I'll write the Swahili words on the board for you."

Mala read the words of the first line, but she could read faster than the teacher could write. She turned to look at the other children. Panda, the tallest boy in the room, was scowling. He was always sure that everything was better in his own language than in any other. Kamina, who lived next door to Mala, and was her best friend, even if she was of a different tribe, was muttering under her breath.

Mala sighed. It must be wonderful to belong to a big tribe and to be able to sing the songs in the language you spoke at home, instead of in the Swahili that all the tribes had to use in the city. In the fifth grade there was no other child but herself from her small tribe and so the songs in school were never sung in her language.

"Now all together," said the teacher, and the children sang the Swahili words.

When classes were over, Mala looked around for her friend, but Kamina was talking with some girls of her own tribe. Mala did not know what they were saying and dropped behind. Kamina and the others began to sing "Joy to the World" in their language. After two stanzas, they stopped. Mala started the third stanza in Swahili, and the others joined her.

"It is lucky the tune is the same, no matter what language we sing," said Kamina in Swahili. Mala felt better.

When Mala stopped in front of her house, Limo was sitting on the steps eating a mango.

"Guess what?" he said.

"You've begun to practice for Christmas," said Mala, sitting down beside him. It was a relief to speak her own language after doing schoolwork in Swahili all day.

"Better than that," replied Limo. "Our grade is putting on a Christmas play in the pageant. I'm going to be one of the Wise Men, and I'm to sing all by myself."

"Well, why not? You are one of the best singers in the school," said Mala. Then she added, "Are you afraid?"

"No, but I'll have to practice a lot," replied Limo. "What is your grade going to do?"

Mala told him about their song. "We're all practicing," she finished, "but only a few will be chosen for the choir."

"You're a good singer. You may be chosen," said Limo.

But Mala was not so sure. "Panda always wants the boys and girls of his tribe to do everything, and so do some of the children from other tribes. I'm the only one from our tribe."

"The best singers should be chosen, no matter which tribe they belong to," said Limo decidedly.

That was what Father and Mother said, too, when the family gathered to eat. The family sang "Joy to the World" twice all the way through in Swahili to help Mala learn it. But they did not know the new song Limo was learning.

After school for the next few days, Mala went to the church to watch the rehearsal of the Christmas play. She listened to all the songs as she waited for Limo. Later she and Limo tried them at home.

In her own schoolroom, it was not always pleasant. When they all practiced together, it was fun. But one day after school, Panda called the children of his tribe around him.

"Our tribe sings best," he said, in a loud and boastful voice. "Even if we cannot use our own language in the church we are the best singers, and we will practice together and get chosen for the choir."

Mala listened as they sang the song, first in their own language and then in Swahili. Panda was certainly a good singer, and others were, too!

Panda noticed Mala standing at the edge of the group. "Go away," he said. "You don't belong to our tribe."

Mala walked away, thinking of Panda's unkind words as she went to the church. The girl who was to be Mary sat quietly by the manger. Another girl, who could not be seen, sang a beautiful song about Mary and the Baby Jesus.

Mala whispered to a girl who was watching; "Which tribe does that singer belong to?"

"Which tribe? I don't know," said the girl, looking a little surprised. "What does it matter? At Christmas we should all be friendly and not think about tribes."

"That is so," agreed Mala, wishing that the children in her class felt the same.

The next day, Mala watched Panda call his group together. She saw Kamina in the middle of another group. Over to the side, under the mango tree, a third group was sitting.

Mala's heart beat fast. The boys and girls of the tribes were gathering in groups, and she did not belong with any of them. That night she told her family about it.

Father looked serious. "I do not like these hard feelings between the tribes," he said. "How can we learn to govern ourselves, if we are so divided?"

"Let's sing," said Limo. "I listened to that song you liked, Mala, the one the girl sings about Mary and the baby. I think I can teach it to you."

Mala felt better as she sang. After they had tried the song several times, Limo sang his song about being a king following the star. Then they all sang "Joy to the World."

"You sing well," said Limo to Mala.

"Oh, I won't be chosen for the choir," she said. "The big tribes will push hard to have their best singers chosen."

Two days later Panda raised his hand in the singing class. "Please, may our tribe sing the Christmas song in our language?" he asked.

"We will be glad to hear it," said the teacher.

The singing was beautiful. "Panda really is the best singer here," thought Mala. She clapped her hands in appreciation, and the teacher and some others joined her.

"Now we would like to hear you sing it in Swahili," said the teacher, and the group sang again. But some children did not know all the words, and even Panda made a mistake. Two other groups sang, first in their own language and then in Swahili. The room was noisy as the last group sat down. The teacher clapped his hands for order.

"Of course, each of us loves his own language best," he said. "But we must choose the best singers for the choir, no matter which tribe they belong to. Let us choose now."

The room became very quiet. Mala looked around. "No one wants to choose someone in another tribe," she thought, "but they are ashamed to call out names of their own tribe because of the teacher's words." She held up her hand.

The teacher smiled at her. Mala stood up and drew a deep breath. "I think Panda is the best singer," she said.

"Yes!" said all the children of Panda's tribe.

"Yes! Panda!" some of the others agreed. A number looked cross, but when the teacher asked those who wanted Panda to be in the choir to raise their hands, there were enough to choose him.

The teacher was pleased. "Panda sings well. Who else?"

"Mala," said Kamina.

There were sounds of agreement over the room.

Mala felt little quivers of excitement all over her body.

"Mala sings very well, and she knows the words in Swahili," said the teacher. "Who else?"

There were no other suggestions. The teacher picked up some paper and tore it into pieces.

"We must choose our best singers so that they can go to

the church to practice this afternoon," he said. "I want each one of you to write eight names on this paper, the four from your own tribe you think sing best, and four from other tribes. Don't count Panda and Mala, who are already chosen."

He smiled at Mala as he handed her a piece of paper. "You will have to write eight names from other tribes," he said.

Mala looked over the class. The first three names were easy. She thought a while before she wrote down four others. She was glad that she could honestly write Kamina's name for the eighth. "It's only because I belong to a small tribe that they didn't mind my being chosen," she thought.

Panda was scowling as he looked over the room, and he scowled even harder when he saw her looking at him. Suddenly he began to write names fast.

The teacher counted the names written on the papers and was pleased. "It's plain enough that you know the best singers when you think about it," he said. He read a list of names, beginning with Panda and Mala. Some of the children chosen were from one tribe and some from another. Kamina's name was among them.

"These children will go to practice in the church after school," the teacher said.

Mala could scarcely wait to get to the church to tell Limo.

"I knew you would be chosen," he said. "You sing well."

Her big brother's approving tone made Mala feel happy inside, but when she went to join her group for the practice, Panda was talking with the boys and girls of his tribe. Two other groups were chattering in their own languages, and no one spoke to her.

"They don't really want me," she thought.

The bell rang for the rehearsal, and the teacher came. He broke up the groups and told the children where to stand. Mala was glad that Kamina was beside her.

Kamina reached out for her hand. "I'm afraid I'll forget some of the words," she whispered nervously.

"Come over to our house and practice with us tonight," Mala whispered back.

At the practice, Kamina did indeed forget some of the words, and so did most of the others, but Mala's and Panda's voices were clear and strong. In the comradeship of carrying the song together, Panda smiled at her.

"I'm glad your class is finished with this tribal trouble," said Father when he heard that Mala had been chosen.

At rehearsals during the next few days, Mala knew that the tribal trouble was far from finished. Except when they were actually singing, the children from the fifth grade were always breaking up into tribal groups, and Mala belonged to none of them. Only Kamina paid any attention to her.

At the last rehearsal, Panda even scowled at her.

"He ought to be ashamed," Kamina said indignantly during a break. "You chose him as best singer."

"He would have been chosen anyway," said Mala honestly. She could not help knowing that she and Panda sang much better than any of the others, but she did not like his scowls.

"I wouldn't want to sing our song without his strong voice in back of me," she went on, "and once in a while when we are singing, he forgets about tribes and is pleasant."

Just then, Limo came rushing up to her. "Come quick!" he said. "Our teacher wants to see you."

"What for?" Mala was so surprised that she did not move.

"Hurry," Limo said, grabbing her arm and taking her along.

Limo's teacher explained. "The girl who sings about Mary is sick," he said. "Your brother says you know the song."

"But, but . . . " began Mala.

"Try it anyway," said the teacher. "If you can't do it, we will have to leave it out of the play tomorrow."

"I can't sing all alone," said Mala, but no one seemed to be listening.

She was led behind a screen. "Stand right here," said the teacher. "When the reader stops reading about Jesus being laid in the manger, you begin to sing."

"I'll help you this time," whispered Limo. "Just pretend there is no one here but us. Then sing your best."

When the boy stopped reading the story, Limo raised his hand, and Mala began to sing. Once Limo hummed a few bars, and once he sang low to help her.

"Very good!" said the teacher, coming around the screen. "How did you learn the song so well?" He didn't wait for an answer. "You can do it in the play tomorrow."

Mala was both pleased and afraid. The singing hadn't been so difficult. And she would be behind a screen and wouldn't

see the people who were listening, so maybe it wouldn't be so bad.

"Will you stay with me tomorrow?" she asked Limo.

"Of course! I can dodge out the side door and be ready for my part when it comes."

All at once Mala remembered that her choir was still practicing. Perhaps now they would choose someone else for her place, perhaps a singer from Panda's tribe.

She started out the side door. Panda came running toward her with a scowl on his face.

"Hurry up," he said. "Our choir is waiting for you." Then he grinned suddenly. "You are the best singer in our class, even if you don't belong to my tribe. You were good in that song. Tomorrow you'll have to hurry to get back so that you can sing with us. Do you think I want to sing in the pageant without your strong voice in front of me?"

Mala rushed into her place in the choir beside Kamina. All the choir smiled at her. Kamina reached for her hand. Mala began to sing with all the rest, "Joy to the World."

NAMES IN THE STORY

Kamina	kah-MEE-nah
Limo	LEE-moh
Mala	MAH-lah
Panda	PAH-ndah
Swahili	swah-HEE-lee

BELGIAN CONGO

The Belgian Congo is a very big country, and the village where Joseph and Lukete live is at least two thousand miles from the city where Mala sang her song. The village lies in the kind of forest that covers much of Africa. There the trees are high and the undergrowth thick. The roads are mere paths. Many of the villages are surrounded by palm trees.

In such villages, the people would follow the old customs of their tribes. Where a school teacher or a doctor or a pastor comes to work in the village, they would begin to learn new ways.

In his village, Joseph would hear only his own language. But he would have to face many problems because a great number of the people around him are not Christians and follow customs based on fear.

4 Beyond the End of the Road

Bump, clatter, bump! The mission truck came chugging along the forest road into the little clearing where the carriers were waiting. Joseph stood watching it with longing eyes. He had never ridden in a truck and he had hoped to have a ride in it today. But instead he had had to walk from the mission station to the clearing with his school friend Lukete.

All around them were giant forest trees covered with vines that trailed down to mingle with the bushes below. There were no houses in sight. The clearing was the end of the road in this part of the Congo.

The missionary doctor and Fumu, his chief medical assistant, who was driving, jumped down from the truck. The ten carriers from the village near the mission, who had walked with the boys, gathered around to help.

"Be careful with those boxes in the front seat," Fumu said. "They have medicine."

"He thinks only of his old medicines," muttered Joseph to

Lukete. He was really fond of Fumu and did not intend him to hear, but Fumu knew the tone, if not the words, and looked at him sternly.

"Just because you had to walk a few miles is no reason to sulk. How do you think you are going to manage to walk many days in the forest, if you mind a few miles this first day?"

Joseph began to work fast at unloading the truck. After all, he was the youngest person in this expedition that was going to villages deep in the forest where there were few Christians. Even Lukete was thirteen, and he was here because he came from a forest village and could help find the paths to them.

"Eleven is very young," the missionary doctor had said, when it had first been suggested that Joseph go on the expedition. Fumu had explained how worried Joseph's parents were about his older sister, Banza, who lived with her teacher husband in one of the forest villages they were to visit. So the doctor had said that Joseph could go along with them to see her, if he would help with the work.

Now the carriers lifted their loads to their heads and began to chant a song as they started down the path.

> We go to the forest.
> We go to the villages in the forest.

The missionary doctor with his gun and two other men with guns walked ahead of the carriers. Joseph and Lukete fell in at the end of the line. Behind them came a man named Kasenda, also carrying a gun.

"Not that I'll see anything to shoot," grumbled Kasenda. "It's the folks up front who will get the meat and make everyone happy."

"We are happy you are behind us," said Joseph. "Suppose a leopard came up in back."

"Not with all the noise we are making," said Kasenda.

Joseph swung along in rhythm with the chant. He even joined in the chorus as it came back through the long line, although he did not feel happy that Fumu was cross at him.

A little later, he was glad to see Fumu waiting by the path.

"Can you carry this for me?" asked Fumu, holding out one of the boxes that he had guarded so carefully in the truck.

"I'll take good care of it," promised Joseph, and was glad to see Fumu's usual warm, friendly smile.

"Some day I'm going to drive a truck as Fumu does," Joseph told Lukete.

In the afternoon Joseph and Lukete heard a shot ahead.

"Meat for supper!" said Joseph.

Word came down the line. "An antelope! But it is small."

"Meat for those who carry big loads," said Lukete, grinning. "But not for boys."

Joseph laughed. It was such fun to swing along the forest road that it did not seem important whether or not there was meat for supper.

When they stopped that night, he was tired in a pleasant way. Kasenda came in after the others, carrying another small antelope, so there was meat for everybody after all.

During the next few days, they stopped often. The drums sounded out through the forest the word that they were coming, and in every village people were waiting for them. Joseph liked to sit with the others while one of the preachers talked to the people. Always they sang songs, and Joseph was glad that he knew the words and tunes well, because the village people needed help with them.

Always, too, there was an eager crowd around the missionary doctor and Fumu. One evening as Fumu was taking care of a sick man, he called Joseph to help. Joseph took one look at the horrible sore on the man's leg and turned his head away.

"Bring me some hot water," said Fumu.

Joseph quickly brought the water, and Fumu handed him

the medicine box. Joseph felt ill, but he tried not to show it.

"That was a bad one," Fumu said as he finished.

"I don't think I'd make a good doctor," said Joseph, a little ashamed. "Lukete likes to help you."

"Not everyone wants to take care of sick people," agreed Fumu. "Perhaps you would rather be a teacher?"

His voice made a question out of the words, but Joseph did not speak his thought—that he wanted to drive a truck.

In the early afternoon of the seventh day, they arrived at the village next to the one where Joseph's sister Banza and her husband lived. Joseph and Lukete sat down to rest.

Fumu came hurrying up. His face was troubled.

"Joseph, there is word here that your sister's husband,

Shundu, is very sick," he said. "Our doctor must stay here to take care of a man who was bitten by a crocodile yesterday. I'm going on at once with medicines, and I want you boys to come. We can get men to bring Shundu to the doctor."

"I'll show you the way," said Lukete.

"Good," said Fumu. "I've asked Kasenda to come along."

They took some bananas and peanuts and started out.

Fumu, with his box of medicine, looked at the sun anxiously. "How far?" he asked Lukete.

"We can get there in two hours if we walk fast," said Lukete.

The four broke into a jogging trot that covered the miles quickly, so the trip took less than two hours. Darkness was coming, and the little fires by the village houses shone out from the yards. But there were only women and children around them. Fumu went straight to the chief's house in the center of the village, where a group of men sat around a fire.

A tall man stood up.

"I bring greetings to your chief and to all the village," said Fumu.

The man answered, "Sit by our fire and tell us of your trip."

"First, tell us about Shundu, your teacher. Word has come to us that he is very sick," said Fumu politely.

"He is better!" said one man in the group.

"He is worse!" insisted another, and everyone began to talk at once.

Fumu spoke sharply. "Take us to him. We bring medicine."

Two men started down the street, and Fumu followed,

with the boys and Kasenda close behind. When they stopped in front of a house, Joseph saw Shundu lying on a mat near the fire. There were only men beside him. Where was his sister?

In the darkness Joseph slipped around in back of the house but could find no one there. As he started back, Lukete met him and pressed his arm.

"Sh, sh!" he said. "Come with me." Swiftly they joined Kasenda, who was standing near some palms.

"There's something wrong," whispered Lukete. "The five men with Shundu are his relatives from a village farther off in the forest. They are not Christians. You stay here and watch them while I try to find the Christians of the village."

Waiting seemed long to Joseph. He could not make out what was happening to Shundu. Suddenly Fumu's words rang out clearly. "I am going to give Shundu medicine whether you like it or not. Then I am going to carry him to the doctor."

Lukete crept up behind Joseph and whispered to him, "There are Christians in a house nearby. Four of them are coming to help take Shundu to the doctor. Come, we will find where your sister is."

The two boys and Kasenda circled the house and went back among the trees. There was no fire near the Christians' house, but several people were gathered there.

"We were with Banza taking care of Shundu, but we were very worried," explained one of the men. "The drums told us that people from the mission were near, and we sent a runner to ask for help quickly. When two strange men arrived, we thought they had come from you. Then they called for the village witch doctor, and we knew we were wrong. Three other strange men came and took Banza when we were not there. They are Shundu's relatives from another village. They would not let us go close to him."

"Where is Banza?" asked Joseph anxiously.

"My wife can show you," the man said. "These men think Shundu will die, and if so, Banza must go with them."

Joseph was trembling as he followed the woman through the trees. It felt good to have Kasenda and Lukete close behind him. Of course he had known all along that Shundu's family was not Christian, but he had not thought about the old tribal custom that a dead man's wife belonged to his family and must become the wife of one of his brothers.

The woman left the path and began to creep through some underbrush. Joseph heard his shirt rip as the sleeve caught on a dry branch, but he scarcely felt the scratch on his arm.

"Where is she taking us?" grunted Lukete.

"Sh, sh!" whispered the woman. "I must see if men are guarding her. Wait!"

The woman disappeared down a bank but soon was back again. "There is no guard," she said. "I think you will be able to break open the door of the hut."

They saw before them a tiny hut in the forest. The bamboo door was tied shut with vines.

"Banza!" whispered Joseph, when the door was broken open. From one corner came a little noise. In the dim light they saw Banza lying there with a cloth over her mouth and her hands and feet bound.

With the help of Kasenda's hunting knife, Banza was quickly set free. "Oh, Joseph, I am so glad you have come," she said sobbing. "What has happened to Shundu?"

"Fumu is taking him to the doctor," answered Joseph.

"Come quickly!" The woman spoke sharply. She drew them away from the hut. They could hear men tramping through the underbrush toward them.

"Go over the hill, and you will find a path that leads back to the village where the doctor is," said the woman. "I'll return the way we came and make a noise so those men will follow me and give you a head start."

They waited, well concealed in the trees and darkness. The woman hurried off, making a lot of noise as she went. Soon they heard the men go crashing after her.

Then Kasenda and the boys and Banza moved quickly away. The forest grew thick about them. Once they stood still, afraid they had lost their way, but Banza took over. "This trail leads to the path," she said. "My garden is right over there."

"We can never find our way back to the village along these strange paths," thought Joseph. "We will surely be caught."

Kasenda must have been thinking the same thing, for he said, "The rest of you go ahead, and I will lag behind. If anyone overtakes me, he will think that I am just a man on the path. If you hear me talking loudly, leave the path and hide."

In a moment Joseph and Banza and Lukete were hurrying

down the path. Once they heard the noise of some animal in the high bush at the side. "A gun in front of us is better than one in back," thought Joseph, wishing Kasenda were there. But they went swiftly on, hearts pounding.

They were almost to the village when behind them they heard Kasenda talking loudly.

They dodged along a little path to the edge of the village. Lukete went ahead to see if it was safe for Banza to enter. The sounds of the night were around Joseph and Banza, but they seemed pleasant, friendly sounds now.

"Listen," said Joseph. "The people are singing together."

"It sounds good," said Banza. "If I only knew Shundu was all right, how happy I would be."

"I think Fumu will have him with the doctor by now," said Joseph.

"There are Christians enough in our village to help carry him here safely," said Banza.

"I hope the woman who brought us to you won't be hurt," Joseph said.

"She will get back home all right," replied Banza. "There are many like her in the village who have not yet declared themselves Christians but who listen and believe. As soon as Shundu is well, we must go back to the village. I wish you would come and help us when you finish school."

"Perhaps I will," said Joseph slowly.

"The village people are coming to meet us," said Banza. "The singing is nearer."

Soon a crowd of friendly people was around them.

"Four men have arrived with Shundu," said several voices.

"Fumu and the missionary doctor are with him. The doctor says he will get well," said others.

"Take me to him," begged Banza.

Food was waiting by the fire, and it looked good to Joseph and Lukete.

"What do you want to do when you are older?" Joseph asked, taking a second helping of rice and antelope meat.

"Make people well, like Fumu," said Lukete promptly.

"I'm going to be a teacher. Maybe even a preacher," said Joseph.

"Not a driver of trucks?" said Lukete, laughing.

Joseph laughed, too. It seemed a long time since he had been angry because he could not ride in the truck.

"Fumu drives the truck sometimes. Maybe I will, too."

"There will be roads everywhere, even deep in the forest, by the time we are grown," agreed Lukete. "We will travel together, and you can preach and I will help the sick ones."

NAMES IN THE STORY

Banza	BAH-nzah
Fumu	FOO-moo
Kasenda	kah-SAY-ndah
Lukete	loo-KAY-tay
Shundu	SHOO-ndoo

SOUTHERN RHODESIA

In Southern Rhodesia, the school year begins in January. The children have a short vacation at Easter and another in August. The long vacation is around Christmas. The story of Bekapi tells about the short August vacation.

The rains stop in April or May and do not begin again until October or November. The cold season comes in the dry months, from June to October.

The African people in Southern Rhodesia live on large tracts of land called reserves. In only a few places can they buy land.

There are schools on the reserves but not enough for all the children. Many of the schools are mission schools, and they have to meet standards set up by the government. They receive grants of money from the government to pay teachers' salaries and to provide new school buildings.

If the children want to go to high school, or even to the upper grades, usually they have to leave the reserves and go to a government school or to one at a mission station.

5 The Herd Boy

Bekapi looked over the dry brown plain to the green spot by the stream that ran through the Southern Rhodesian reserve. Yes, the cows were there. Bekapi did not count them, but repeated their names to himself as he looked.

"Broken Horn isn't with the rest," he said to his older brother, who was lying by the big baobab tree.

"Go find her," said Dutsa, without looking up.

Bekapi frowned but did not answer. He knew what to do without being told. But Dutsa was four years older than he and liked to boss.

Usually Dutsa went to school each morning, walking two miles each way. But today was the beginning of his vacation. For weeks Bekapi had been looking forward to his brother's company and help with the herding. But Dutsa wasn't being much help today, he thought, as he walked toward the stream to look for Broken Horn.

The missing cow was not far away, and Bekapi soon had her

back with the herd. He sat down near Dutsa and began to draw
a picture in the sandy soil. Dutsa wrote some words in the
sand with his finger. Bekapi watched him.

"What does it say?" he asked, standing up to look.

"If you weren't so stupid, you would know," said Dutsa.
"Have you forgotten everything you learned at school?" He
sounded cross, but he really liked to explain things and he told
Bekapi what each word was.

Bekapi was too angry to listen. He gathered the cows together and started toward home full of rage. As though he
could help it that he had been sick and out of school the year
before. By the time he was well, he knew he couldn't pass the
school examinations. So he had begun to herd his father's
cows. Now Dutsa seemed to think he was good for nothing
but herding, and only Funase, his younger sister, knew how
much he wanted to go to school.

Dutsa caught up with him, whistling cheerfully, and began
to talk about the sports at school. As Bekapi listened, his anger
slipped away. It was fun to have his brother with him after all.

"Father is here!" he cried joyfully as they came in sight of
the four little mud houses that made up their home. Their
father was now working in the city and did not get home very
often.

Dutsa ran ahead, and Bekapi went on to shut the cows in
their pen. By the time Bekapi joined the happy group in the
yard, Dutsa was talking fast, telling Father about school.

"I'm the head of my class," he said proudly.

Father looked pleased, but he turned and put his hand on Bekapi's shoulder. "Now show me the cows," he said.

Dutsa started to go with them but turned back when his father paid no further attention to him.

Father patted each cow and praised Bekapi. "They look well. Do you like to take care of them?"

"Yes," said Bekapi. "But I want to go to school again."

"That's one reason I came home," said Father. "You have grown tall lately, and you are strong again. After supper, I have some news to tell the family."

Bekapi was so excited that he could scarcely eat the good cornmeal mush and bean sauce that Mother and Funase had ready. When the food was finished, Father began to talk. He told how lonely he felt in the city without his family.

"But if I stay home, our few acres would not produce enough to feed us and send you children to school. So I want to move to the city. I have already found a house for us."

Mother looked as if she had expected something like this to happen.

"Now you can go to school, Bekapi," whispered Funase.

"This is good news," said Dutsa. "In December I will finish the school here on the reserve. I want to go on to high school."

"I have thought of that," said Father. "But I have thought even more about Bekapi. He needs a chance to catch up in school. I will take him with me to the city tomorrow."

"Why Bekapi?" demanded Dutsa. "If you want someone to help you get the house ready, I can go. I'm on vacation."

"Who will take care of the cows if I leave?" asked Bekapi. He was not sure whether he was happy or afraid at the thought of going to the city.

"Dutsa," said Father. His eyes were twinkling.

"But—but—but—I have to go to school," sputtered Dutsa.

"Not during vacation," Father said. "But it won't be for long. Later one of the village men will care for our cows with his. Dutsa, you can do the herding during this vacation. You can live here with Grandmother while you finish your last term. Your mother and Funase will come to the city as soon as they can get ready."

"What will Bekapi do?" asked Dutsa. "He can't start school until January."

"He will go to the vacation school at the Christian center in the city," said Father. "He needs to get used to school again. You must take your turn at looking after the cows."

Father's voice sounded a little stern, and Dutsa did not say anything more. When the two boys went to bed, he would not talk, and Bekapi felt uncomfortable. The next day was not much better. Bekapi was glad when it was time to leave.

It was dark when they arrived in the city. Bekapi was almost too tired to look at the house that was to be their new home.

But the next morning Bekapi was eager to see everything. He walked to work with Father, watching at each turn and wondering if he could ever find his way alone.

When they parted, Father said, "Go up the street and turn left, and you will see the Christian center. Go inside and tell the young man there your name. He knows you are coming."

Bekapi followed his father's directions. Outside a big building some children were gathering. They went inside, and soon
Bekapi could hear them singing. Once he peeked in the door,
but there was no young man in sight, and he was afraid to go
inside, so he left.

Bekapi walked along the street admiring the things in the
store windows. He had never seen so many people. It was very
exciting to watch the trucks and cars hurry by. The houses
were all alike, and twice he made a mistake on a turning and
had to go back and start again. He began to worry about what
his father would say about his not going into the center.

But when Father got home, he was not cross. He only said,
"I suppose any boy needs one day to see the city. Tomorrow
you will go to the center."

Bekapi did not sleep well that night because the city was so
noisy. There was loud laughing and talking in the next house.
People walked by and woke him up. He longed to be back at
home where it was quiet. Surely it would have been better if
Dutsa had come with Father.

The next morning Father got up late and had to hurry so
fast to his work that Bekapi could scarcely keep up with him.
Bekapi walked on more slowly to the center. When he saw the
children going inside, he gathered up his courage and followed
them. He found himself in a room full of children who were
laughing and talking. By and by they sang, but Bekapi did not
know the song.

A young man began to tell a story to the children. "That must be the man Father meant," Bekapi said to himself.

After the story, the children divided into groups. Some went to one corner, and some to another. Bekapi did not know what to do. The children of his own age followed the young man teacher into another room. One boy gave him a friendly smile as he went by, but Bekapi could not smile back. He looked toward the outside door. It would be easy to slip out now without speaking to anyone.

But Bekapi knew that his father expected him to stay. If he wanted to learn, he had to make a start. Besides, he really was interested in finding out what these boys and girls were going to do. So he slipped into the room behind the last one.

Near the door the boy who had smiled at him and some others were getting out paper and pencils. Some of the papers already had pictures on them.

"I could make a better elephant than that one," thought Bekapi, excited at the possibility of having a whole sheet of paper and a pencil to use. He saw some crayons and little jars of colored paint. He moved nearer to look, and the boys made room for him.

"I must find the teacher first," said Bekapi and walked slowly across the room. The teacher saw him and came toward him.

"Are you Bekapi?" he asked.

"Yes," said Bekapi.

"Your father told me you were coming," said the teacher, smiling at him. "Which group would you like to join?"

"Oh, please, may I draw?" asked Bekapi.

"Yes, indeed. I'll introduce you to Stephen."

Stephen turned out to be the boy who had smiled at him, and Bekapi was glad.

Bekapi scarcely dared to begin making marks on the clean sheet of paper. But he soon found it wasn't so different from drawing on the ground, except that he couldn't rub out the wrong lines as easily. His first picture was of Broken Horn.

"That's good!" said Stephen. "Why don't you put some grass around her?"

He rolled a green crayon across the table. Bekapi tried it on the edge of the paper and reached for a brown. The grass wasn't green on the reserve at this time of year.

A bell rang, and the drawing class came to an end. Stephen showed Bekapi where to put his picture. Everyone gathered around the teacher, who told an exciting story of a man who had taken the Bible to people in a land where they had never heard about Jesus.

The teacher called on one boy to read from the Bible. For a minute Bekapi's heart pounded. Suppose he was asked to read! Perhaps he had better tell the teacher that he could not read well. But he felt too shy to do it.

The next day the teacher told a story as soon as the boys and girls arrived. Again Bekapi was frightened when the teacher wanted someone to read the Bible, but Stephen was chosen.

When the story was finished, the teacher said, "Today each of you must decide which group you want to stay in. Some of you will be making plays from the Bible stories you hear, and some will be drawing pictures showing places where the Bible has gone. On the last day of our school, we'll invite some of our friends to watch the plays and see the pictures that we have made."

Bekapi was sorry when Stephen decided that he would rather be in a play than draw pictures. Still, Stephen didn't draw very well, but his voice was clear and strong, so that in a play everyone could hear what he said.

Bekapi decided that he must ask the teacher not to call on him to read. It would be better than being embarrassed in front of the whole group.

"Oh, don't worry about that," said the teacher, when Bekapi spoke to him. "Not all the boys and girls can read well. Your father told me about your missing school. Some night we will practice a little reading together, all by ourselves."

That night when Bekapi went home, he was happy to find that Mother and Funase had arrived. He wondered whether Funase could get into the school this late, but he took her with him the next day.

"Oh! Oh! How do you know which way to turn?" she said on the way. "I will never be able to find my way home."

"I will wait for you," replied Bekapi, feeling pleased to know so much. Then he asked the question that had been bothering him. "How is Dutsa?"

"At first he was so cross he wouldn't say a word, but last night he talked as much as usual." She grinned. "By the time school begins, I expect he will tell you he is the best herder of cows on the reserve."

Bekapi laughed, for Funase made her voice sound like Dutsa's when he had boasted that he was top of his class.

It was fun to show Funase over the Christian center. There were two groups of children her age, and there was a place for her.

When the time for drawing came, Bekapi practiced sketching people. They were not as good as his animals. But if he was going to make pictures to illustrate stories, he would have to learn to draw people.

"Animals don't take the Bible to others, and they don't listen either," he said to Stephen, who had come from his group to watch. "But I don't know how to draw people."

Stephen laughed. "Draw your cows over here on the side. Then have the people listening over here. The teacher says men have taken the Bible everywhere."

Bekapi remembered the pastor who had come to their part of the reserve. He tried to draw a man who looked like him. And this time the drawing looked like a man.

The days went by quickly. On Sunday, the family all went to church, and Mother learned about meetings at the center that she could attend.

The teacher remembered his promise and helped Bekapi with reading one night.

"Perhaps if you study well and I help you in the evening, you won't be very much behind when school starts," he said.

The next week end Father went back to the reserve, and Bekapi waited anxiously in the city for his return.

"How is Dutsa?" he asked as soon as he saw Father.

"He's all right. School starts for him tomorrow," replied Father. "You have learned much, but Dutsa has learned even more in the last three weeks."

"What has he learned?" asked Bekapi, surprised.

His father laughed. "How to take care of cows, for one thing. He's going to take care of them during the long vacation, too.

He doesn't like it, but whatever Dutsa does, he does well, and he wants me to give him the money I would have to pay a village man to look after the cows. He sent you a very special message."

"Tell me," said Bekapi eagerly.

"He said, 'Tell Bekapi to study hard and then come and spend the long vacation at Grandmother's with me. I will teach him while we herd the cows together. Then he will not be ashamed at school because he is behind in his class.' "

"Dutsa will teach me more than I can learn in the city during vacation," said Bekapi slowly.

"Yes, but you do not have to go unless you want to," said his father.

"I will go," said Bekapi. His eyes began to shine. "It is exciting in the city, but by and by the rains will begin and the grass will grow green at home. I will be glad to see Broken Horn and the other cows again. When the new year comes, Dutsa and I will come to the city together."

NAMES IN THE STORY

Bekapi	bay-KAH-pee
Dutsa	DOO-tsah
Funase	foo-NAH-say

UNION OF
SOUTH AFRICA

Johannesburg is a large city in the Union of South Africa. Parts of it look like any city you know, with big buildings, store windows full of beautiful things, wide streets, churches, and schools. But one reason that Johannesburg is large is that it is in the center of a gold mining district, and some of the mines are actually within the city.

The African men who come to work in the gold mines leave their families back home in the villages. They work in the mines for eighteen months and then return home with the money they have earned. When they feel they need money again, they go back to the mines. Each man who wants to go to the mines has to have a physical examination before he is accepted as a worker.

Kamba came from a village in the Union of South Africa. Other workers in the mines come from Mozambique, which is under Portuguese rule, or from different parts of Africa.

6 Kamba at the Mines

Kamba was big and strong for his age—at least for the age his uncle said he was. No one was sure just when Kamba had been born, except that it had been at the beginning of the rains, the year they had come so late and everyone had been hungry because of the poor crops.

Kamba didn't care how old he was, but he did want to go to work in the mines in Johannesburg.

"I am as tall as you are," he said to his cousin, who had just come back from eighteen months' work there. "And I'm strong, too."

"The work in the mines is hard," said his cousin. "I'll be glad to stay home for a while."

Then his cousin went on to tell of the city—its streets, its games and dances and movies. The life in the city sounded wonderful to Kamba and a lot more fun than life in the village where he lived. As for the hard work, Kamba and his twin sister Tola had done plenty of that since their parents had died and they had come to live with their uncle, who saw to it that they earned their keep.

Kamba walked along the sandy path to the building where the men who wanted to go to the mines were being examined. He stood on the edge of the group, wishing that he could be one of them.

"This month there aren't as many men applying as are needed," a man near Kamba said to his neighbor.

Kamba quickly made up his mind to try his luck. He stepped to the end of the line. Zungu, the man in front, was the father of his sister's best friend. He was tall and broad shouldered, which made Kamba feel small, but just then a man no taller than he took the place behind him, and he felt better.

The line moved on, and Kamba's turn came to be examined. The man measured his chest and looked him over. Kamba tried to make his voice sound deep. When the examination was finished, he was pleased to find himself holding a paper saying he could go to the city on the train Monday.

He walked home, half afraid to tell the family what he had done. But he blurted out the words, "I'm going to work in the mines."

His uncle frowned. "You are too young!" he declared.

"Who will help me here?" complained his aunt.

Kamba turned to Tola and saw a look of sadness come over her face. For a few minutes he was sorry that he was going. He would be lonely without her.

"I'll miss you," she said later, when she handed him his

food. "But you must learn to read and come back and teach me."

"What?" He was so surprised that he nearly dropped his bowl. "What do you mean? I am going to work, not to learn."

"Mina's father learned to read while he was at the mines," said Tola.

"Mina's father is going back to the city," said Kamba, remembering that Zungu had stood in front of him in the line.

"Yes, and Mina is sad. Her father was teaching her to read. I wish I could read."

"Why?" Kamba had occasionally wished he could read. Some day he might get a good job if he could read. But why should a girl want to read?

"I want to read the Bible," replied Tola. "Mina's father brought a Bible home. Please bring me a Bible when you come back, Kamba."

"Don't be silly," said Kamba. "You couldn't read it. I'll bring you some beads and a dress."

Her aunt called sharply, and Tola hurried to help her. Kamba finished eating and went off to find the other boys. Some of them looked at him with envy when they heard that he was going to the city. Others thought he was foolish. Kamba did not care. He knew they all had fathers and mothers to look after them, and they never had worked as hard as he.

On Monday morning, Kamba made a bundle of his blanket, with his extra shirt and shorts inside. He walked the six miles to the station. The night before, Tola had begged to go with him to the train, but he had said no, that there would be no other girls. Now he saw that he had been wrong. Many mothers and wives and children were there to say good-by to the men and boys. Seeing them made him lonely, and he was glad when he saw his sister pushing through the crowd.

"How did you come?" he asked.

"I walked with Mina and her family," Tola replied. "I was afraid I would miss you." She handed him a package of food.

The train came puffing into the station, and the men climbed on. The women and children called out last messages, and the men leaned far out the windows.

"Good-by! Good-by!" shouted Tola. "Be sure and buy me a Bible."

The train was full, but Kamba found a place on the floor and used his bundle to lean against. A young man was dozing beside him.

The men who had been in the mines before told the others about the city. By and by, some went to sleep. Kamba dozed, but the train bumped and shook him so that he sat up again.

Zungu came over and squeezed in beside him.

"Would you like to live in the room where I am going?" he asked. "The men from our tribe who are Christians asked to live together so they could help one another."

"It would be good to live with men who speak our language," said Kamba slowly. He started to explain that he was not a Christian, but Zungu stood up and said, "Think about it and tell me what you have decided when we get to the city."

Zungu walked away, and Kamba saw him stop and speak to another of the boys.

The young man beside him sat up. "You won't have any fun at all if you go with Zungu," he said.

"Why?" asked Kamba.

"Oh, they have classes and study at night. On Sunday, which is the only day we have for fun, they go to church."

Kamba opened his package of food and ate. It made him think of Tola and her request for a Bible. If he went with Zungu, he could learn to read. He noticed the young man beside him looking hungrily at his bread. He broke off a piece and gave it to him.

The train bumped on, darkness came, and Kamba slept a little. First he thought he would tell Zungu that he would like to live with him. Then he thought that he would say no. He changed his mind several times during the night, but by the time it was morning and they reached the city, he had decided that it would be better to go where he could do as he pleased. He looked around for the young man but could not see him. Finally the train stopped, and everyone began to push toward the door.

Kamba stooped to pick up his bundle. It was not there! It must be on the floor somewhere. He looked for it all around but could not see it. The crowd in the car moved toward the door, and in spite of Kamba's protest, he was pushed along.

As he stood in the car door, Kamba saw his companion of the evening before. Under his arm was Kamba's bundle.

Kamba made a quick leap to the platform and, putting his head down, butted his way through the crowd of men. Fortunately, a big fat man blocked the way of the young man with the bundle. Kamba came up in back and gave him a good punch in the arm and grabbed the bundle.

"So that's how you have your good time, is it?" he asked.

The young man struggled to hold the bundle, and a man grabbed him. Another man grabbed Kamba, who now held the bundle.

"What is inside the bundle?" one of the men demanded.

"A shirt and a pair of shorts," said the young man.

"Yes, a shirt and a pair of shorts," said Kamba slowly. The young man had guessed right. But then Kamba had an idea. "What color are the shorts—blue or khaki?" he asked.

"Blue," said the young man.

Kamba began to undo the bundle. The young man gave a hard jerk and was gone in the crowd.

"Well, I guess that proves the bundle is yours," said one man laughing, as Kamba held up a pair of green shorts.

"That was smart," said the other, "but take care. You look young to be coming to the mines."

Kamba pushed his way across the platform. Men were speaking different languages. Kamba stopped, confused, wondering what to do next. He was relieved to see Zungu, standing tall above the others, and hurried toward him.

"Oh, there you are," said Zungu. "Do you want to go along with me?"

"Yes, please," said Kamba, and he followed Zungu to one of the waiting buses.

At the mine compound, there were long, low buildings with many rooms. Kamba did not think the room where Zungu led him looked very pleasant. Concrete bunks for forty men lined the walls. A round stove in the center and two benches and a small table completed the furnishings. Kamba was glad to go out with Zungu to find out about his work.

The room seemed more cheerful that evening when it was full of laughing men. They shouted with joy when they saw Zungu and included Kamba in their enthusiastic greetings. Kamba enjoyed the gay songs they sang and the stories they told. Someone began a hymn, and after that Zungu prayed. There was more singing, but Kamba, tired from his long trip, pulled up his blanket and went to sleep on his bunk.

The next few nights Kamba was too tired when he finished work to do anything but eat and go to bed. Gradually he grew used to the hard work.

One night on his way home, he met two boys about his age and had a good time laughing and talking with them.

On Sunday, he went with them to the dances. Men of one tribe after another did their tribal dances. It was fun to watch.

The next Sunday, Zungu said as Kamba left the room, "Better try to get back in time for our church service."

"All right," agreed Kamba. But he and his friends began to practice dancing, and before Kamba knew it the time for church was long past. There was no use in going home, and he walked around with his friends.

Suddenly a man dashed out of a house and almost knocked Kamba over. Another man followed close behind. The first one fell, and the other jumped on top of him.

"A fight! A fight!" cried someone, and a crowd quickly

gathered. Several men had been drinking, and they began to take sides with the two fighters.

"Here come the police!" said one of Kamba's friends. "Let's get out of here!"

The three boys slipped away from the crowd just as two big policemen pushed their way to the fighters.

As he neared his own room, Kamba felt a little uncomfortable, but Zungu did not say anything about his missing the church service. All the men were talking about the movie that a missionary was going to show the next night.

"Maybe it is only for the Christian men," Kamba thought, wishing that he could attend. He had never seen a movie.

To his surprise and delight, he found that the movie was to be shown outdoors and that anyone could come. A big crowd gathered to see the pictures. Some of the pictures were of people in other parts of the world. Some told the story of a boy and a dog. Kamba watched in amazement.

The next night, Kamba stayed in the room and listened as Zungu helped two men learn to read. Kamba decided he wanted to learn to read, too. He stayed inside the next night and the next, and studied. Soon he would not have missed the class, no matter what was going on outside.

When he bought the first reader, he thought of Tola. "I'll keep this for her," he said to himself. "I'll teach her to read it when I go home. She can't read the Bible the very first thing."

The next Sunday morning, Kamba went out to see his friends. "I'm going to the church service," he said.

"Oh, come on with us," they urged him. "The dances are more fun!"

"Some other time," said Kamba and hurried back to the room. Men from other rooms had come, and the bunks and seats were all taken, but two of the men moved closer together and made a place for him.

One of them whispered, "The missionary is here."

Kamba looked up front. Zungu was there. With him was a pastor of their own tribe and a white man, a young missionary with very fair hair. Kamba had never seen anyone like him before and watched him all during the next song. After the preacher prayed, the young missionary stood up. He said a few words of greeting in Kamba's language. Then he spoke in English, and the preacher interpreted what he said.

At first Kamba was confused, listening to the English words of the missionary and then to a sentence or two of his own language from the preacher. But soon he became interested. The young man told about his own home in North America and how much he liked his new home here in Africa.

"As I came in to this place, I saw many, many people." The young missionary held his arms out wide. Kamba thought of all the men outside. "Some of them are gathering together to worship God as we are. But many do not know anything about him. We can tell them about him. Each one of us knows a few people he can tell about God."

Kamba thought of his two friends. "I couldn't tell them much about God yet," he thought to himself, "but I could ask them to come here with me and listen and learn to read, too."

As soon as the meeting was over, the men crowded around to talk with the preacher and the missionary.

Zungu said to Kamba, "The preacher has brought books for us. I need someone to help me bring them in."

Outside there were two bundles of books. The preacher handed one to Zungu, and the missionary gave one to Kamba.

"That missionary will soon know our language, and we can help him learn it," said Zungu to Kamba. "He is coming to our room every two weeks to teach us about the Bible."

Zungu opened the packages. In one were schoolbooks.

"You will want to buy this one soon," he said, holding up a blue reader.

"Yes," agreed Kamba, but he was looking at the Bibles in the other package. He thought of Tola. "Please keep one of the readers and one of the Bibles for me," he begged. "I'll save my money and pay for them soon. I want to be able to read them both and to teach others to read."

NAMES IN THE STORY

Kamba	KAH-mbah
Mina	MEE-nah
Mozambique	moh-zam-BEEK
Tola	TOH-lah
Zungu	zoo-ngoo

ANGOLA

Kasitu and his friends live in Angola, a country under the rule of Portugal. All the children learn to read and do their schoolwork in Portuguese, not in their own tribal language.

Much of Angola lies on the high central plateau of Africa, where many kinds of fruits and vegetables grow well. There are few large cities in this part of Africa, and most of the people live in villages.

It may seem strange that an uncle should have as much power as Kasitu's, but in many tribes in Africa, a father's brother would have as much say as the father himself. In some tribes, the mother's family has the right to direct affairs. Almost always relatives have a share in the responsibilities of bringing up the children. This is often a good thing, because it means that children always have care. But when part of the family has become Christian and part still believes in the old ways, trouble often follows.

7 Kasitu

Kasitu stood in front of the grass roofed church in his village in Angola and looked anxiously down the road.

"You don't believe that the mission station people are really coming here to give us trees, do you?" asked one boy in a mean way.

"Listen," said Kasitu, holding up his hand.

"I hear a horn!" shouted another boy. "They are coming!"

"The truck is coming!" Everyone took up the cries.

"I knew they would come when they promised they would," declared Kasitu triumphantly.

The village people began running to meet the mission truck. It moved along slowly, partly because it was heavily loaded with young fruit trees and partly because of the children in front of it. Behind the first big truck was another, full of men and boys.

"I do hope John is there," thought Kasitu.

Until two years ago, when his teacher father died, Kasitu

had lived at the mission station, and John, the son of the pastor, had been his best friend.

"Kasitu! Kasitu! Here I am!" John jumped from the truck, and the two boys greeted each other warmly. Then John went to work with the other men and boys, unloading the truck.

"I promised I would work hard if I could come with the agricultural class that is bringing these trees," he explained to Kasitu. "The class is big this year, and I was afraid my father would say that there was no room in the truck for me."

Kasitu greeted other friends from the mission station and then began to help John. Soon everyone was working. The agricultural missionary and John's father directed the work.

The agricultural students showed the village people how to plant the little trees. Before long, mango, orange, and lemon trees were in the ground, and also banana and bamboo shoots. By dinner time, the trees had been planted around all of the twenty-two houses, the church, and the school building of the village. The village families were happy to pay the small cost of the trees that came from the mission nursery.

"Some day the trees will yield enough fruit for all the people in the village," said Kasitu's mother. She had helped in the hospital at the mission station before her marriage and knew about the foods that keep people strong. During the planting, she and the other women had been preparing food in the schoolyard for the village folks and their visitors.

"Meat!" Kasitu wrinkled his nose as he smelled the food.

"Yes, the missionary shot a big antelope this morning, and

two men brought it here as fast as they could," said John. "Um! The food does smell good!"

Kasitu's mother piled cassava mush high on the plates. John's father asked the blessing. Then he and the missionaries and teachers sat down at a long table under a grass roof with the important men of the village. All the other folks sat in little groups on the ground.

When Kasitu and John had eaten all they possibly could, they lay on the ground and talked. John told Kasitu about the new tractor that had lately arrived at the mission station.

"That tractor can plow more ground in a day than all of us schoolboys together can dig," he said. "So we have more time to care for the gardens. We can grow more, too."

"I wish I could see the tractor," said Kasitu wistfully.

"Oh, you'll see it soon," said John. "You'll be coming to the mission school before long."

"I'm not sure I can go," Kasitu replied. "How will Mother and the children get along without me? Mata is the only girl, and she is too young to help. So I have to do the work."

Kasitu did not really mind helping his mother, who had to work harder than the other village women because she had no husband to help support her four children. The village boys often made fun of Kasitu for doing girls' work. His brothers, Emanuel and Davida, who were eight and six years old, were not much help, and his sister Mata was only four.

It felt good to be talking again to a friend like John.

"My father promised yours that he would see you got

through school," said John. "Of course you are coming to the mission."

Kasitu sat up and hugged his knees. "I know it was planned that I was to go to the mission station when I finished school here in the village. But my uncle keeps saying I must come to his village."

"Your uncle isn't a Christian, and there is no school in his village. You shouldn't go with him," said John.

"Uncle says we all belong to him. We are afraid that he will make trouble for Mother unless I go to him," said Kasitu.

At that moment, the call came that the trucks were ready to leave. "I'll talk to my father about it," John said soberly.

Mata came running up, and Kasitu put her on his shoulder. The students piled into the trucks and began to sing as they moved off. Kasitu turned toward his house with Mata.

It was only a few days later that a man brought a message that Kasitu's uncle would soon be coming.

"Your father wanted you to go on to school," Mother said to Kasitu. "Maybe it would be wise to send you to John's father soon. Yet that might make your uncle very angry."

"Then he would come and get me," said Kasitu. He picked up the water jug and started down the path toward the stream. He liked to get the water in mid-afternoon, before the village women and girls went to get their water.

Mata came dancing after him, and he took hold of her hand. He saw his two brothers playing down the path. "Mother told you to bring wood for the fire," he scolded them.

The boys laughed and started to pick up the twigs and little branches near the path. Mata followed them and began collecting twigs, too.

"Take care of her," called Kasitu.

Kasitu filled his jar at the stream and hurried back. As he came in sight of the cassava garden, he saw Davida standing near the pole fence that was put up to keep out the pigs. Somewhere close by, Kasitu could hear a child crying. Mata! Where was she?

Kasitu put his jar down and began to run. As he ran, Davida suddenly disappeared from sight.

"Someone must have dug a trap near the fence to catch animals," thought Kasitu. "The children have fallen into it."

The crying grew louder as Kasitu approached the fence. He saw a hole and cautiously peered into it. He could see Mata lying on the ground and crying.

Davida was standing up in the hole, looking surprised. "I was telling Mata not to cry, and I slid down," he explained. "I'm not hurt, but I think she is."

"Where is Emanuel?" demanded Kasitu.

"He has gone to the village for help."

"Good, then I am coming down. Move over by Mata."

Kasitu was relieved to find that the hole was not quite as deep as he was tall. He stooped to touch Mata, and she cried out loudly.

"It's her arm," said Davida. "See?"

"Yes, my arm," sobbed Mata.

"Maybe it's broken," said Kasitu. "I hear people coming. I will lift you up to them."

One man and then another peered down the hole. "Three of you in the trap!" exclaimed one.

"I came down on purpose," said Kasitu. "Can you reach down to take the children?"

He dug a place for his foot in the side of the hole and helped Davida up so the men could pull him out. Then he lifted Mata. When she was safe above, Kasitu was helped out.

Mother came running down the path. She looked Mata over anxiously. "I am afraid her arm is broken," she said. "We must find men to carry her to the mission hospital."

"Wash your face and brush the dirt out of your hair," she said to Kasitu, when they were at their house. "You must go to the hospital with Mata."

"It's you she will need," objected Kasitu.

"But your uncle is coming. He might take all three of you boys to his house. So you must go."

Kasitu said nothing more. He helped his mother tie a blanket between two poles like a hammock, so the men could carry it over their shoulders. Everything was ready by the time the carriers arrived. Mother put Mata gently but firmly into the hammock and paid no attention to her cries that she did not want to go. The men jogged off down the path to the hospital.

Kasitu's mother managed to smile at him. "I am sorry Mata had to break her arm, but as long as it's done, you have a good excuse to stay at the mission until I send for you."

Kasitu hurried after the men. It was only six miles to the mission, and he and the carriers ought to be there by dark. The men walked fast, and Kasitu had to run part of the time to keep up with them.

When they reached the mission station, the African nurse looked at Mata's arm and sent for the doctor.

"There's nothing to worry about," the nurse told Kasitu. "We will put her to sleep and set her arm. Tomorrow she will need you to keep her happy."

But Kasitu waited until the doctor came before he walked to John's house. Suddenly he realized he was very tired and had a few bruises himself from his slide into the hole. He was glad to be able to rest.

The next few days Kasitu divided his time between the hospital and seeing the mission with John and the rest of his old friends. A carpentry shop and new dormitories for boys had been built since he had been there. Best of all he liked the tractor. He could have spent all of his time watching it make the land ready for gardens.

He would have been perfectly happy if he could have forgotten his mother and brothers. Suppose his uncle took both the boys and perhaps even his mother home with him! After all, his uncle was his father's older brother, and according to tribal law he had the right to say what the family should do.

"Your mother is a strong Christian," said John's father. "Do not worry. She has stood firm for two years since your father died and will keep on doing so."

"I wish she would move back here," said John's mother.

That night Kasitu got a surprise. Mother and the boys came to the mission. "Your uncle arrived, and he wasn't as cross as he often is," she told Kasitu. "He was impressed by our village's new fruit trees. He says he is coming to the mission to see if he can get some."

"Will he want me to go home with him?" asked Kasitu anxiously. "I want to learn about farming here. Maybe some day I can even run the tractor."

"He will probably try to make you go with him," said Mother. "Be careful, and don't go far from here. If he once took you to his coffee farm, I would have hard work to get you back home again."

During the next few days, Kasitu did not go out into the fields unless John's father was there, too. Mata was doing very well in the hospital, so Mother began to help the nurse. One night Mother told Kasitu that the doctor and nurse had asked her to work at the hospital all the time and that she had agreed. This work would pay her enough to take care of her family.

"Now we can live at the mission, and you and the other children can be sure of the Christian education that your father and I planned for you," Mother said, smiling at Kasitu. "I really didn't know how I was going to manage in the village without you next year."

His mother's words made Kasitu feel happy and important. Then one day his uncle suddenly came up behind him in the field. Kasitu looked quickly around in alarm, but when he saw John's father not far away, he greeted his uncle as politely as he could.

"I have been looking around the farm," said his uncle. "The missionary says I may buy some fruit trees soon. I think that this is a good place. I had heard that all you did here was to study out of books."

"We learn many things," said Kasitu. "I want to learn them all, and I want to run the tractor."

His uncle frowned a little. "All right, learn them," he said. "But after you have learned them, you must come to me."

"In a few years I will be older and strong enough to decide for myself," thought Kasitu. "Perhaps I will even learn how to make my uncle understand about Christian living as well as good farming."

He smiled up at his uncle. "Come with me to see the tractor," he said.

NAMES IN THE STORY

Angola	ang-GOH-lah
Davida	dah-VEE-dah
Emanuel	eh-mah-noo-ELL
Kasitu	kah-SEE-too
Mata	MAH-tah

CAMEROUN

Work among the people who have leprosy occupies an important place in medical missionary work throughout central Africa. For many years, doctors have studied and worked to find out the best ways to help these people. Now they are happy that there are medicines that make it possible for many patients to go back and live with their families. The medicines do not completely cure the patient, but the disease becomes inactive.

The scene of this story of Mepui and his family is in the French Cameroun. This family was fortunate that it lived near a leprosy colony where the father could have good care and learn a trade at the same time.

8 Two Kinds of Fun

Mepui dived to the bottom of the stream and grabbed his friend Afan's foot.

"A crocodile has you!" he cried, as both boys came up sputtering.

"This is the last day of your fun, Mepui," said Ela, who was already dressed. "You had better make the most of it."

Mepui splashed out of the water and faced him. Of all the older boys, he admired Ela the most, but Ela was not always pleasant to him.

"What do you mean?" he asked indignantly. "This is a time of great happiness in our family."

"Oh, of course you are happy that the hospital doctors have cleared up your father's leprosy," said Ela. "But your father has become a Christian!"

"What's the matter with being a Christian?" demanded Mepui.

"Oh, your father will want to know what you are doing all

the time," said Ela. "And wait until he finds out you have been skipping school. No more swims! No more trips to town! We will miss you, Mepui."

Mepui glared at Ela, who only laughed and walked away.

Mepui and Afan stood in the morning sun to dry before they put on their clothes.

"Don't mind Ela," said Afan. "He is only teasing, and he is too big for you to fight." He looked at Mepui's shirt, which had a big hole in the back. "Perhaps your father will buy you a new shirt."

Mepui and Afan walked up the path to their village that lay in the French Cameroun. Afan's house came first, and Mepui went on alone to his own little house.

His five-year-old sister Menge was sitting on the ground chewing some sugar cane. Mepui sat down beside her and picked up a stalk of sugar cane. Their mother put a dish of food between them.

"Eat," she said. "We have a long walk ahead of us."

"Father is coming home today," sang Menge happily.

"Menge doesn't even remember when Father used to live with us," thought Mepui. He looked at his mother and knew by her face that she was remembering the long years they had been alone, while Father had been in the village where the leprosy patients lived. Now Father was able to come home.

"Hurry up and eat," Mepui said to his sister. They both ate fast and soon were ready to leave with their mother.

The path was easy at first, but it grew rougher as they

went up one hill and down another. The sun was hot, and Mepui was glad when they moved into the shade of the forest. But he was glad again when they came out into the village clearing. He knew that in the forest dangerous animals might be lurking among the trees. But all they had heard was the chattering of monkeys.

When they came to the big village where the leprosy patients lived, they stopped near the dispensary. A great crowd had gathered around it to greet the patients who were being dismissed that day. Two medical attendants of their own tribe were in charge of the dismissals.

Two women came out dancing and laughing, and a young man followed. Next were two children, and their waiting families laughed and danced for joy.

Mepui watched anxiously for his father. Menge danced up and down in excitement and kept asking, "Where is Father?"

Then suddenly Mepui saw Father standing tall and straight in the doorway, carrying a wooden box.

"There he is!" he cried and ran toward him.

Father put his arm around him. Mother began to dance for joy. Father laughed to see them so happy, but tears stood in his eyes when he noticed that his little daughter shrank from him as from a stranger.

The missionary doctor came to say good-by.

Father said, "I have been made well and I give thanks to God and to you."

"We all give thanks to God that you are better, not only in

your body but also in your spirit," said the missionary doctor.

"Take what you have learned of God to others," said one of the attendants.

Mepui walked proudly along toward home, carrying the box that his father had handed him. He had never felt so happy in his life. Before they had gone far, Menge was walking close beside her father.

That night the family rested at a friend's. Early the next morning, they were on the path again and soon reached home.

A few of the village people greeted Father, but some would not come near him. Mepui was angry when he saw them staring at his father.

"Don't they know that you are well?" he demanded.

"They know it in a way, but they cannot really believe it," explained Father. "For hundreds of years no one got over this disease. These people cannot understand about the wonderful new medicines. Give them a chance to get used to me."

Next morning when Mepui woke up, he found that his mother and Menge had gone to work in the garden. His father was in the yard, and the wooden box was open. In it Mepui saw a hammer and a number of other tools.

"I learned how to use these tools at the colony," his father explained and then asked, "What class are you in at school?"

"The second," said Mepui slowly.

His father frowned. "That's not very good for a boy who is almost twelve," he said, "but I know you have had to help your mother a lot while I was away."

"I'd like to stay home with you today," Mepui said, picking up his father's hammer. No one else in the village owned one. He longed to try it.

"We will have plenty of time together," said his father. "You must go to school every day."

Mepui hurried off. When he came to the place where the paths divided, one going to the school and one to the river, he hesitated. Ela would probably be at the river having a good time. Ela had skipped school so much that last year the teacher had told him that he could not come at all unless he were more regular. So Ela had stopped school altogether.

"School is only for little boys," he used to say scornfully to the boys. Mepui sometimes felt that Ela was right.

Today Mepui did not take the path to the river because Father had sounded serious about school.

When he entered the classroom, the teacher asked where he had been lately. Mepui had a bright idea.

"Father came home yesterday," he said.

The teacher smiled. "I am glad," he said. "I will expect you to be in school every day now."

Mepui soon found that he would have to work hard to catch up with his class, and he put his mind on his studies.

When he arrived home that afternoon, Mepui saw several boards in the yard.

"These belong to the headman," said his father. "He has wanted a new door for a long time, but there was no one here who could make it."

"You can make it! You can make it!" chanted Menge, dancing about the yard and running over to her father.

"Yes, I can make it," said her father, giving her a hug.

Mepui felt a little jealous. "Menge was afraid of Father yesterday, but now she acts as if he had always been here," he thought. He wished he could show how glad he felt that his father was home.

Father turned to talk to him. "I made many doors, tables, and benches while I was getting well. Your mother brought me so much food from her garden that I could save the money I earned at work, and I bought my own tools."

Mepui watched his father smooth a board with a plane. Oh, how Mepui wished he could hold the plane! Suddenly his father handed it to him. "Hold it and look at it," he said. "I will show you how to use my tools. Here is the hammer."

He found an old piece of board and three nails and showed Mepui how to use the hammer. "Be careful and don't pound your thumb instead of the nail," warned Father.

Mepui pounded the nails into the board, took them out, and pounded them in again. It was great fun! He wished that Ela could see him. But it was Afan who came and watched.

Mepui could hear his mother singing while she cooked. She had not sung for a long time. Soon she called them to eat.

After the family finished their meal, Father brought his Bible and read from it. Then he thanked God that they were together again.

Menge was almost asleep. Mother picked her up and took

her inside the house. Father handed the open Bible to Mepui.

"I want to hear how well you can read," he said, pointing to a place to start.

Mepui was glad the story was that of the Good Samaritan, for he had studied it in school. Even so, he stumbled over several words. He wondered what his father would think.

"We must practice reading every night," Father said. "I never had a chance to learn to read until I went to the leprosy colony. You will have lots of time to study now I am home."

It made Mepui uncomfortable to have his father think that he was behind in his studies because he had spent so much time helping his mother. Down in his heart, Mepui knew that he had often skipped school to be with Ela. What fun it had been to swim with him and to walk to the nearby town to see the sights!

Though he missed the good times with Ela, Mepui was having fun in his own yard now, and he hurried home every night after school. Afan usually went with him, and so did several other boys who wanted to see the tools. Mepui showed them how to pound nails. Father let each one look at the saw and the plane while he stood nearby. When the boys had gone, Father let Mepui try the saw and plane.

"If only Ela would come some day," Mepui thought, "how happy I would be." But only once did he see Ela, watching from a distance.

Father finished the door, and the headman was so pleased with it that he ordered a table.

With the money Father earned, he bought food to eat and a new dress for Mother.

Every day some of the village people came to Mepui's yard to hear Father tell them what he had learned about God. Mepui listened with pride.

The trader at the crossroads wanted Father to make him some shelves. Mepui went to the store each day after school to help make them.

One afternoon as he came in the door, Mepui heard his father say to the trader, "My son works hard. I will take my pay in clothes for him."

Mepui looked longingly at a red and white striped shirt, but shorts were more important, and he chose khaki ones.

"Soon we will have enough for a shirt, too," said Father.

Mepui turned away from looking at the shirts and saw Ela coming in the door. As he started toward him, Father said, "Measure this board and mark where I should saw it."

Mepui unrolled his father's measure and leaned over to measure the board. When he looked up, Ela was there.

"Can you really tell how long it is?" asked Ela.

"Yes," said Mepui. But Ela's question had disturbed his measuring, and he had to begin again. He felt a little annoyed because he wanted Ela to think he could measure well. "Put your finger here and hold the measure," he said, and to his surprise, Ela obeyed.

Ela watched while Mepui marked the board for sawing.

"Let me measure it," said Ela. "Show me how."

Mepui was pleased. It was good to have Ela acting like a friend again. He was glad when Ela's measurement came out exactly like his own.

Ela looked at Mepui's father fitting a shelf into the wall. "Does your father cut where you measure?" he asked.

Mepui hesitated but told the truth. "He measures it again. But he says he would measure twice even if he were doing it alone. It has to be exactly right. In school I used to think it didn't make much difference whether my figuring was right or not, but it sure makes a difference when measuring a shelf."

Ela frowned, and Mepui was sorry he had mentioned school. He began to talk fast about the tools. "Come over to our house some afternoon when we have finished here and see them," said Mepui.

His father smiled at Ela and said, "Yes, come any time."

Ela did not say he would, and though Mepui watched for him, he did not come.

"I wish Ela would come to our house," said Mepui to Afan.

"I think that he would like to come," said Afan.

One morning, Mepui's father said, "You don't have to work all the time. When school is over today, why don't you go play with the boys?"

"I will go for a swim," said Mepui.

It had been a long time since he had done much more than jump into the river to wash and cool off. Today he would go for a real swim, and perhaps he would see Ela, too.

After school, Mepui and Afan took the path to the river.

Halfway there they saw Ela standing under a tree. "I'll race you to the river for a swim," Mepui called to him.

Of course Ela won the race. His legs were longer, and Mepui had known that he would, but he did not care. The water felt good when he plunged in, and he swam around and around. Some other boys came, and they all began to play a game.

But when Ela climbed out and sat down on the bank, Mepui followed him.

"Why don't you come to my house?" Mepui asked. "My father would teach you how to use the saw and plane."

Ela said slowly, "I would like that. I wish I hadn't left school. I can't even read."

"Come to our house, and Father will help you. We practice reading every night," said Mepui. He had a comfortable feeling that his father would teach Ela if he was asked.

Ela walked back home with Mepui. Father saw them coming into the yard and said, "How about learning to use the plane?" Mepui was delighted. This would be even more fun than swimming.

NAMES IN THE STORY

Afan	AH-fahn
Cameroun	kam-ROON
Ela	AY-lah
Menge	may-NGAY
Mepui	MAY-poo-ee

NIGERIA

Nigeria is a country on the west coast of Africa that will be independent soon. It has been under British rule, and the educated people speak English. Many young people have gone to England and some to America to study. There is a university in Nigeria, and young people like Yabo and Abibola will have a good chance to get an education. However, there are still many children who do not go to school at all.

The people of Nigeria do not all think alike about the government of their country. Besides these differences of opinion that divide them, several big tribes find it difficult to work together.

Differences of religion also divide the country. Some people follow the old tribal customs. Some follow the Muslim religion and some, the Christian. A number, like Yabo's father, have no religion. There are more Muslims than Christians, and as a result, the Muslim young people often have a better chance of getting a good job than the Christians. Christian young people, on the other hand, are more likely to have a chance to go to high school and college and to become leaders.

9 Yabo's Present

Yabo hurried along the narrow market street of her city in Nigeria. She was eager to be home in time to greet her cousin Abibola, who was coming with his father to spend the night at her house. Tomorrow, school would start for them both. Abibola would go to the boys' boarding school on the other side of the city, and she would go each day to the school near her home.

Yabo dodged around a woman who was carrying on top of her head a flat basket piled high with bright red and green and blue cloth. For several days Yabo had been looking at the wares spread out on the ground and on tables in the market, hoping to find exactly the right present to buy for Abibola with the pennies she had saved. But she never seemed to find anything good enough for her cousin.

Under a roof of mats was a display of earrings and beads, but today Yabo would not stop to look, even when the market woman called to her. Next were a few little paper covered books. Abibola might like a book, one with stories in English, but how could she tell which one? Perhaps the one about airplanes?

"Yabo!" The voice behind made her turn in surprise.

"Abibola! I was hurrying home to see you."

"You didn't look as if you were hurrying," said Abibola in a teasing tone. But he added quickly, "Come along. I have something to tell you."

Yabo had difficulty in keeping up with Abibola as he pushed through the crowded street. Once she lost sight of him behind one of the many booths that jutted out into the narrow street, but she saw him again as they came out onto the wider road that led to her house. Abibola stopped under a red flowering tree.

"What's the matter?" asked Yabo.

"Father won't let me go back to school," he said. "That is, not to the same school."

Yabo looked at him in astonishment. "But Abibola, this is your last year! What are you going to do?"

"I'm to go to the new government school," Abibola answered. "Oh, that isn't too bad, for this government school prepares for the university. It is the reason Father is making me change that I don't like, Yabo!"

Yabo looked at him and waited for him to go on.

"He is making me change because my school teaches Bible," he said. "Lots of Bible."

"Of course," said Yabo. "It is a Christian school. I've studied

Bible in my school every day for four years. What difference does that make?"

"I've had it every day for six years," said Abibola. "Father has never said anything before, but now . . ." He hesitated and went on slowly. "Yabo, my father has decided to become a Muslim."

"Oh, no!" Yabo never felt she knew Abibola's father very well. He was tall and serious and not at all like his brother, her own jolly father, who was always laughing and telling about the funny things that happened in his shop.

"But you won't have to be a Muslim," she said slowly. She did not know much about Muslims, for no girls of that religion ever came to her school. Indeed, most Muslim girls never went to school at all. But she had often seen the Muslim men stop their work to pray in the market place, always kneeling with their faces toward the faraway sacred city of Mecca. Somehow she could not imagine Abibola becoming one of them.

"No," replied Abibola firmly. "No, indeed, Yabo. I am going to be a Christian." He stopped and lifted his head a little. "That isn't quite right. I am a Christian. I decided last term."

Yabo looked at him with respect, for she had sometimes thought of doing the same thing, only there didn't seem to be any hurry.

"Is that the reason your father is making you change your school?" she asked.

"I don't think so, for I haven't told him. But maybe he guessed it. I hope it has made some difference in how I act. Perhaps I'm a coward not to tell him."

Yabo had a sudden idea. "Do you have a Bible?" she asked.

"No. When I decided to be a Christian, I began to save to buy one, but I haven't enough money yet."

"I'll help you," said Yabo. "Listen, Abibola, when you found me, I was looking for a present for you, only I didn't know which book you would like best. If I give you my money, you can have your Bible without waiting."

Abibola looked at the one shilling and the pennies Yabo put into his hand. "Oh, thank you," he said. "This is the best gift you could give me."

"We had better hurry home," said Yabo. "I'm glad you found me, or I might have bought you the book about the airplanes."

She watched Abibola draw a little bag from under his loose blue coat and put the money into it. Then they hurried along the row of mud houses that stood so close together that they touched. When they reached Yabo's home, they found no one in the first small room. But they could hear loud voices coming from the enclosed yard beyond. Yabo's mother was working in one corner, and her younger brothers were playing nearby. The two fathers were sitting in a shady spot under a roof made of mats. Yabo greeted her uncle, and he said a word or two to her before he began talking to her father again.

Abibola stood at the edge of the mat shelter, not sure

whether or not he should join his uncle and father. Yabo knew that she must go and help her mother. She went slowly across the yard and for once was glad that her uncle's voice was loud, so that she could hear what he said. He was talking about the advantages that came to those who were Muslims.

She could hear her father's deep laugh, and it reassured her a little, though she could not hear his answer.

"Don't worry," whispered her mother. "Your father will never become a Muslim. He has said so many times."

Yabo did not feel entirely comfortable as she helped make the food ready for the men. She knew that her father and uncle always did everything together.

Abibola had sat down with the men. Even in her worry, Yabo could not help laughing when she heard her uncle's loud speech about the need to study hard.

"Abibola will study well no matter where he is," she thought proudly. But she knew that Abibola would never do all the things his father and her father wanted. They were both good businessmen and often discussed how much more money they would be able to make in trading cocoa when Abibola was ready to add his learning to their shrewdness and hard work.

Long after the food was eaten and the housework finished, Yabo could hear her uncle's voice and now and then a rumble that was her father's laugh.

"I hope Mother is right," she thought, as she turned from one side to the other in bed. It was true that she, too, had heard her father say many times that he would never become a

Muslim, but she had also heard him say many times that he would never become a Christian either, and she would like him to be that. He did not mind that her mother went to church sometimes, but he himself would never go unless it was to a big meeting or something exciting.

Up until now, Yabo had taken it for granted that if she wanted, she could go on to the high school, even though not many girls did. She knew that it would make a big difference to her as a girl if her father became a Muslim, much more than it would to Abibola because his father had become one. Abibola was two years older and besides, he was a boy and could better live his own life.

The next morning, when Abibola and his father were almost ready to leave, Yabo saw Abibola look hard at her and disappear into the yard. She slipped after him.

"Yabo," he said quickly, "you must buy the Bible for me. There may be no chance at my school. Here, take this." He handed her the bag of money. Yabo slipped it into her dress.

"If this isn't enough money, I will try to have more next time I see you," whispered Abibola.

His father put his head around the corner. Yabo tried to make her voice steady. "You will come to see us on your day away from school, my cousin?"

"I will come," replied Abibola in a firm voice.

"He will come," said his father, "but I have told your father that he must not go to church."

Fortunately for Yabo there was no need to reply. She knew

by the shocked expression on Abibola's face that he had not
heard this news before.

"It is lucky that he didn't say Abibola mustn't have a Bible,"
she thought as she watched her cousin and uncle leave.

Yabo hid the money away in her cupboard. It seemed a lot
of money, but when she went into the bookstore at her
school, she found it was not enough.

"It is enough to buy this New Testament," said the big
girl who was selling books.

Yabo hesitated. Would it be better to buy a New Testament than to wait?

"I'll think about it until tomorrow," she said.

That night as they were working together, her mother said, "You are very quiet. Are you worried about Abibola?"

"Yes," said Yabo.

"He will be all right," said her mother. "You must listen well to everything at church and tell him."

Suddenly Yabo thought of something. If she brought a New Testament home, there was no place that she could put it where her mother would not find it. And she did want to buy a Bible. Surely she could trust her mother to understand. So Yabo explained her plan.

"Yes, indeed. Abibola must have a whole Bible," said her mother. "I would give you the money, but I used all I had to buy your school clothes. We will ask your father for some when he comes."

"Oh, no!" cried Yabo in alarm. "Perhaps he will tell Abibola's father."

"Don't be silly," said her mother severely. "You know your father better than that. He hasn't changed just because his brother has become a Muslim."

Her mother must know her father better than anyone else, thought Yabo. But later as she listened to her mother explaining the difficulty to him, she felt somewhat scared.

"How much money do you have, Yabo, and how much does the Bible cost?" her father asked kindly.

Yabo brought the bag and watched while her father counted the coins carefully. Then he put a piece of paper money on the table and took all the coins.

"That will be all you need," he said. "Abibola must have a Bible. He will need a good one to read, for he will probably become a Christian."

There was a question in his voice, but Yabo did not answer it. It was for Abibola himself to say what he was, not for her.

"Never mind," said her father, and he laughed his deep laugh.

"I wish you would become a Christian," said Yabo suddenly.

Her father looked surprised. "Why?" he asked. "Don't you like your father the way he is?" And he laughed again.

"Of course I do," she said quickly, but then she went on slowly. "Maybe I want you to because I need you to help me."

Her father stopped laughing. "That is as good a reason as any I've heard," he said. He took another bill from his bag. "Buy yourself a Bible, too. I want to see how well you can read."

"Oh, thank you!" cried Yabo. She knew that her father could read enough to manage his business and that he hated to admit that he could not read everything.

It was fun to choose the two Bibles the next day. When she came home, she put Abibola's away carefully and sat down to read her own.

"I wish I knew how to explain things to Father," she thought. "Perhaps Abibola will help me."

Although Abibola was very happy to see the two Bibles when he came on his day off from school, he did not think that he could explain much to his uncle.

"Can a boy talk wisdom to a man?" he asked. "My school is good. There are Christians and Muslims in it, and ones like your father who think that the old ways of our tribe are enough for them."

That night Yabo listened as Abibola told her father that he was a Christian.

"I love my father," he finished. "I do not want to make him angry, but is it right not to tell him?"

"That is the trouble with you Christians," said Yabo's father. "You are always wondering what is right. Muslims recite their prayers and say everything is the will of Allah. That is the end of it."

"I may even become a Christian minister," said Abibola. "My father would not be willing to pay for schooling if he knew that."

Yabo's father frowned. "Your father and I need you in our business," he said. "But if your father is angry and disowns you, then you are to be my son until he takes you back again."

"He will be too angry to take me back again," said Abibola. "Muslims often turn away their children who are not Muslims."

"Those who have been Muslims for many generations may do so," agreed Yabo's father, "but there are many tribal families in which Muslims and Christians live in peace under one roof."

He laughed his deep laugh and went on. "Your father will be angry, but he will not let me have his son forever, when he is so proud of you and has pitied me because my oldest child is a daughter."

He looked teasingly at Yabo. She did not mind the joking words too much, for she knew that her father was as fond of her as of her younger brothers.

"Don't worry," her father said to her. "I am well enough off as I am, but this I will promise you. If I become anything, it will be Christian."

He turned back to Abibola. "Your father will talk loud and long about his new religion. But he won't do much. Perhaps you had better read to me from your Bible so I will understand your new ideas and be able to talk with him about your belief."

Yabo brought the two Bibles and called her mother and brothers. She looked over Abibola's shoulder to see where he would choose to read. It was the Sermon on the Mount. She followed the words carefully in her Bible. She must study hard so that she could read as well as Abibola. Then she could read to her father and mother every day.

NAMES IN THE STORY

Abibola	ah-bee-BOH-lah
Yabo	YAH-boh

LIBERIA

Liberia is different from most of the countries of Africa because it is independent and has always been so. It was settled by freed slaves from America who went there during the first half of the nineteenth century. Tribal people were already living there, because the land had long been their home.

In Liberia today, there are two groups—the Americo-Liberians and the tribal people. For a long time there were difficulties between the two groups. The Americo-Liberians often looked down on the others. The tribal people felt resentful toward the Americo-Liberians.

But this is changing. The two groups are learning to get along together. More and more of the tribal people are going to school and getting educated. Some have duties in the government. The president of the country is anxious that people of both groups should make progress in all ways.

10 The Bridge of Vines

"I'm going back, Masita! I'm afraid! I'm going home."

Masita stopped on the vine bridge over the river near her village home in Liberia. She turned to encourage her little cousin Musu. But the vine bridge swayed, and she grabbed for the long vine tendril at the side. That was no help, for the frail support pushed out with her weight, and she pulled her hand back quickly.

"I'm afraid, too," she called. She heard Musu running back to the village, but she stood still, trying to steady herself on the uneven floor of the bridge, undecided whether to follow her cousin or not.

"Come on, Masita! Don't look back. Don't look down. Look at me!" Her brother's voice was sharp, and Masita looked ahead. She was more than halfway across, and it would be foolish to turn now. Besides, hadn't she decided that this year she would go to school even if it did mean crossing the bridge every day?

Masita kept her eyes on her brother as she moved ahead. He was all the way across and ready to climb down from where the vine bridge was fastened to the big tree on the other side.

He held out his hand, and Masita was glad to take it. The two children climbed down the four steps of the stick ladder to the ground.

"Aren't you afraid?" asked Masita.

Her brother did not answer. He laughed and ran ahead to join the other boys. Masita did not mind. She was eleven, and her brother was two years younger, but all the year before he had crossed the bridge to go to school with the older boys from their village.

It was early morning, and the grass was still wet with dew. Masita walked between the coffee trees and along the road to the white school building. She felt in a corner of her wrap-around dress to make sure that her money was safely tied there. The sum was not large, but everyone in the family had helped to get it. Even her old grandmother had given her a few pennies when she had sold some rice.

At the school Masita paid the money for her schooling. She watched the teacher write her name in a book and was told that she would be in the first grade.

In her class there were only about half as many girls as boys. Masita found that some of the children were quite small. "They are almost babies," thought Masita, "younger even than Musu." But she knew they were the size you were supposed to be when you started to school. Masita was glad to see one girl bigger than herself sitting behind her and hoped she would be a friend. The teacher called her Beke.

Some of the children could speak no English, since at home they used only their own tribal language. The teacher put four of the boys and two of the girls in a beginners' group by themselves. They did not seem to mind when he told them that they would have to learn to speak English before they could learn to read it, but they were small and had plenty of time to study.

"That's where they put me last year, big as I am," muttered Beke from behind. "I ought to be in the next grade now."

Masita was worried lest she be put in the beginners' group. But her brother had taught her many English words, and she had practiced saying sentences to him. When it was her turn to answer the teacher's questions, she spoke slowly and tried to make the English words come right.

The teacher smiled at her. "You may go in the class that will learn to read," she said. "You are Peter's sister, aren't you?"

"Yes," said Masita.

"He did well last year and was promoted," said the teacher. "I think you will learn quickly, too, if you come every day."

Masita was proud that her brother was in the next grade, but she was not sure that she could do as well.

"I will try," she said carefully, thinking of the bridge.

The smallest girl in the room spoke the best of all. Masita listened to her with surprise. She had never heard anyone speak so well in English, unless perhaps the teacher. The girl was such a pretty little girl, too, with a red dress trimmed with white, and red ribbons on her braids. Esther was a pretty name for her, and Masita had never heard it before.

"Red shoes, too," whispered Beke. "Thinks she's smart! She comes from the coast, and her father has a store. She—"

The teacher looked sternly toward Beke, and she stopped whispering. Masita was glad, as she wanted to listen to the teacher.

She was not sure that Beke was going to make a good friend after all.

There was no real work on this first day, since it took a long time to write down everyone's name and find out about each one. At recess, when Masita reached the playground, she saw the little girls in a circle around Esther. As Masita watched, one girl reached out and gave Esther a push. Masita could not hear what was said, but Esther started to run away from them.

Masita held out her hand to Esther. "Let's play a game," she said in her language.

"Esther doesn't know anything but English. She can't play the game," said one girl.

"We can show her how," said Masita, holding tight to Esther's hand. "Come on, if you want to play."

Soon the girls were laughing in the game, Esther with the rest. As they stopped, Masita saw a girl about her own age coming toward them. Esther dropped Masita's hand, and ran to the girl, speaking fast in English.

"Thank you for being kind to my little sister," said the girl slowly, in English.

Masita could not think what to say in English. She looked at the girl's blue dress and white beads. She must be in a high grade, since she had come from the other side of the yard.

"What grade?" Masita managed to ask.

The other girl looked puzzled and then smiled and answered, "The sixth, and my name is Sarah. What is yours?"

Masita said her name and was glad that Sarah did not ask her grade.

After school Masita started home alone. A little way along, the boys jumped from behind a tree to startle her, but she was glad to see them. It was easier to cross the vine bridge with two of them waiting for her on the other side and two behind her. She tried to act as though she did not mind when the bridge swung back and forth.

Back at home, Masita enjoyed sitting in the shade of the porch of the little mud house and speaking in her own language while she ate the rice her mother had saved for her. Musu came and sat beside her, asking questions about school while Masita cracked palm nuts to sell. She took the kernels carefully from the shells, because the trader would buy only whole ones. She would sell the nuts to get more money for school.

Musu was very interested in hearing about Esther.

"Maybe I'd have to go in the class to learn English, if I went to school," Musu said.

"Probably," agreed Masita cheerfully. "But you had better do it this year while you are little. Then when you are as big as I am, you will be in a high class, maybe in . . . " She hesitated a minute and finished, ". . . the fourth." She had been going to say, "the sixth, like Sarah," but even the oldest boy in their village was only in the fourth, so perhaps she had better not make it higher than that.

"I'll go tomorrow." Musu drew a deep breath and added, "I am so afraid on the bridge, Masita, but I do want to see Esther and learn English."

The next day Musu kept her promise and went to school with Masita.

Sure enough, Musu had to go in the beginners' class to learn English before she could enter first grade. When recess came, she and Esther played together and soon were good friends. Sometimes they could not understand each other, but Esther helped Musu with English and Musu drew Esther into the group.

Masita was often lonely. In class she was busy studying, but at recess she did not know what to do. Sometimes she played with the little girls. Sometimes she talked with Beke, although she did not enjoy it. Beke was always stirring up trouble. When she was around, the younger girls were likely to be mean to Esther.

One day when Masita protested, Beke said angrily, "Why don't you go play with Sarah then, if you think her folks are so nice? Likely she wouldn't have a thing to do with you. She and Esther think they are better and know more than we do, just because their great-grandfathers came over from America."

Masita did not know what to answer. Beke's words might be partly true, but she remembered that her father often said that the people of their tribe were learning more and more and that many of the Americo-Liberians were helping them.

Masita left Beke and walked across the yard. To her surprise, Sarah came to meet her.

"Esther has been teasing to walk part way home with Musu and see the wonderful vine bridge," she said. "Mother said she could go today if I went with her. Will you take us?"

"Oh, yes," said Masita eagerly.

When school was over, the four girls started along the road. The two little ones ran ahead, and Sarah and Masita talked.

"I wish you were in my class," said Sarah. "Ours is mostly boys, and I am lonely."

Masita looked at her in surprise. It had never occurred to her that Sarah could be lonely, too. She pointed to the bridge.

"That is the reason I'm not in a higher class," she said soberly. "I wish I had been brave like Musu and started to school while I was little."

"Musu has you to help her," replied Sarah. She looked at the vine bridge dangling over the stream. "I wouldn't dare to go across even now."

Esther liked climbing the little ladder to the bridge. She took a few steps on the bridge, then turned and came down again.

Masita and Musu tried to act unconcerned while their friends watched them cross the bridge.

"I'm afraid Father won't let me come when the rains start," said Musu to Masita, after they had waved good-by to Esther and Sarah and had started on to the village.

Masita had been thinking about that difficulty. The year before during the rainy season Peter had not always been able to go to school. Maybe if she studied hard, she would be promoted, even if she did miss some days.

Two days later it rained heavily. Every day after that there was rain. The river began to rise. Instead of being a gentle little stream, it became a rushing torrent that swirled up over

the rocks by the bank where the women pounded clothes to wash them. The water surged up toward the vine bridge, and Musu's father said she could not cross. The next morning, when Masita looked at the water, she was not sure that she ought to try it either, but she kept her eyes on the trees ahead and did not look down.

"I won't be able to go much longer," she thought sadly.

As she walked into the schoolyard, Sarah came running.

"Oh, Masita!" she cried. "My father is going to ask your parents to let you come and stay with us while the rains are heavy. He is going to ask your father today."

"How wonderful!" said Masita. "I do hope I can come."

When school was out, Masita hurried home. She found her father and mother and Musu's father and mother and her grandmother all talking together about the invitation.

Masita listened anxiously. To her joy, Father said she could go. Mother looked doubtful, but Grandmother stood up for Father's decision.

"What fun you will have!" said Musu. "I think Esther might have asked me, too."

"You are too small. I wouldn't let you go, even if they had asked you," said Musu's father.

Masita was very happy, but she did feel sorry for her little cousin. "Come and help me pack," she said.

When Masita told the news at school the next day, Beke sneered.

"You will be nothing but a servant. When those coast people ask children of the tribes to live with them, they make them work hard."

"Sarah's family isn't like that!" cried Masita indignantly. Yet she feared that Beke might be partly right. Although Masita knew one woman who took good care of three tribe children who lived too far away to walk to school, she also knew a boy who was made to work very hard in another home.

In spite of her fears, Masita went to Sarah's house.

Several times in the next few weeks she thought of Beke's words and laughed to herself. Sarah's father and mother treated her as they did their own children. It was true she worked, for Sarah's mother insisted that everything be clean and neat.

For the first time, Masita slept in a bed instead of on a mat on the floor. She tried to act as though a bed were an ordinary matter for her.

On Sunday, Masita went to Sunday school with Sarah, and afterwards to church with the whole family. The preacher spoke in English, but one man stood at his left hand and another at his right, and each told the people in their own language what had been said.

"When I go home, I will tell Father and Mother about hearing a sermon in more than one language," thought Masita.

In spite of all the excitement of living with Sarah, Masita was glad when the rains began to slacken. One Sunday she was surprised to see her father in church.

"Next week you are to come home," he said.

"I have had a good time, but I'll be glad to come," said Masita. "I have learned much more English, but I want to speak my own language and be at home."

"Good!" said her father, looking pleased.

A week later, when Masita walked down the road toward home with Peter, she was surprised to see her father and Musu's father just before she reached the bridge.

"We are going to move part of the village to this side of the river," explained Musu's father. "Then the village children can go to school without crossing the bridge. As soon as it is dry enough, I will build a house here."

"How happy Musu will be!" cried Masita in delight. She looked inquiringly at her father. "What will we do?"

"First I'm going to build a house for your grandmother here," he said. "She wants to go to church. Your mother and I can stay with her sometimes."

"So can I," said Peter. He looked at his sister and laughed. "Of course, I'm not afraid to cross—" he began.

"Of course not," said Masita quickly.

"But I really haven't liked crossing the bridge on bad days," he admitted, "and I'm going to have to study hard to be promoted after missing those worst days."

Masita followed Peter across the bridge. She would always be welcome at Sarah's, but it was good to know that she could stop at her grandmother's house in bad weather. She heard a glad shout and hurried to meet Musu, who was running toward her.

NAMES IN THE STORY

Beke	BAY-kay
Masita	mah-SEE-tah
Musu	MOO-SOO

TYPE: ELECTRA 11 POINT ON 13 • MANUFACTURED BY
SOWERS PRINTING COMPANY • JACKETS AND COVERS
BY AFFILIATED LITHOGRAPHERS, INC. • TYPOGRAPHIC
DESIGN BY MARGERY W. SMITH • BINDING DESIGN
BY LOUISE E. JEFFERSON